Southword *36*

Southword is published
by Southword Editions
an imprint of the
Munster Literature Centre
Frank O'Connor House
84 Douglas Street
Cork City T12 X802
Ireland

www.munsterlit.ie

 @MunLitCentre

 /southwordjournal

#Southword

Issue 36
ISBN 978-1-905002-59-7

Editor
Patrick Cotter

Production
James O'Leary

Seán Ó'Faoláin International Short Story Competition Judge
Paul McVeigh

Gregory O'Donoghue International Poetry Competition Judge
Brian Turner

Thank you to Elizabeth Murtough and Anne Kennedy for their technical assistance

Cover image: *fatali (life after fire)* by Evgeniy Shaman

The Munster Literature Centre is a grateful recipient of funding from

Comhairle Cathrach Chorcaí
Cork City Council

CONTENTS

PLEASE SUBSCRIBE

By subscribing, you will receive new issues of *Southword* straight from the printers, as quickly as we will ourselves. Your subscription will also help to provide us with the resources to make *Southword* even better.

Rates for two issues per year:

Ireland, UK, USA	€20 *postage free*
Germany, France, Italy, Spain	€24 *postage free, tax-inclusive*
Rest of the world	€30 *postage included*

For subscriptions and renewals visit www.munsterlit.ie – payment accepted by PayPal.

Southword may also be purchased issue by issue through Amazon outlets worldwide and select book shops in Ireland, the UK, Europe and the USA. We keep an up-to-date list of supporting book shops on the www.munsterlit.ie subscriptions page.

THREE POEMS
Kim Addonizio

HAPPINESS REPORT

I was happy when I was drunk one night in 1985
squatting in the already pee-wet grass next to Jill Somebody
outside the graduate student poetry reading

and in spite of going off my medication
I was happy today under the hot shower, and again licking cappuccino foam
in front of the air conditioner before I went outside
and sweated through my new shirt like a lying politician in a TV interview

I felt happy while buying the shirt though it wasn't a pure happiness
stained as it was with a price tag
It's hard to find a happy artist because art
requires suffering, goes one theory nearly everyone buys into
getting free subscriptions for their friends

On the wall of the museum, patrons could finish the sentence
Before I die I want to. . .
and someone wrote *be happy*
and another *eat KFC*
but a third wrote *cancel my life* and I bet that person was an artist
or at least more sensitive than the one with a bucket list
that included tortured chickens
I hate the term bucket list
which sounds to me like molded plastic instead of stainless steel and pocked
with little holes your feelings fall through

Some artist said it's better to fall from a great height
but I don't know about that

Maybe great happiness is an abyss
Maybe looking down all you see is a big lake and your own face floating there
looking back and smiling
so it's probably best to back away slowly

I don't know why the Constitution talks about the pursuit of happiness
since the framers were really talking about property
Life, liberty, and property
Maybe I would be happier if I owned some
Some of my ancestors owned slaves
and some were Italian peasants
Maybe all freedoms are stained

Before I die I'd like to see some changes made
but it's probably too late
just as it's too late to drink myself to death at a young age

That day at the museum I thought *I want to climb to a great height and then fall through
        myself the way a man falls through me when I'm happy and in love*

Now I only want espresso and a little foam
To stay in bed all day, Christmas lights blinking against the August heat

Pigeons landing outside on the air conditioner walking around making soft noises
        and then fucking off

Someone screaming in the street who isn't me

The Miraculous

The band starts the song over,
the rhythms still wrong, sounds that will never
alchemize to music. My brother's
new liver is failing. There's someone's loud lover
swearing to Christ and the bar to get sober
but the moon is being smothered
by the trees and there is no ladder
far enough. I go down to the mouth of the river

ugly with waste. Yellow foam and trash. A tanker
crawling the horizon. What does it bear—
oil or chemicals. I was taught a man could walk on water.
That if I listened, and unhinged my heart, I'd hear
a presence stirring the air. And I do: God, the murderer
making things perfectly clear.

STILL TIME

In Severn's letters Keats is still alive, though coughing blood,
one day he's better, then things look very bad and if you stop
reading he's still lying there, calmer again and clearer
before they take his body out and burn the wallpaper.
In books you fall in love with, you always slow down
a few pages before the end but then there you are
with only the back-cover blurbs that say
This story will make you cry and maybe an outdated photo.
When you photograph the famous fountain the water
stops moving, but water never really stops moving.
Your plush lion swirled away, your parents floated off okay but also
that wine stain on your shirt only looked permanent.
After the horrifying bats in the cenote, little gold-flecked fish appeared.
You finally stopped sobbing in the bathroom at weddings.
You can't go back to 1821 and invent streptomycin,
or stop the poet's kindly doctor from bleeding his patient,
but you can climb the stairs to that room in Rome
and see the flowers on the ceiling, the same ones Keats held
for weeks in his fevered gaze. That's as close as you can get.
Go home. Your miserable bitch of a neighbor is gone,
carried out and never to return.

When All the Stars Burn Down
Ron Rash

There had been no shade as they built the dock, and though they wore sunscreen, the skin between shirt and ball cap had been burned to the color of brick. Brent and his father rubbed calamine lotion on their necks each night, but the skin remained tender to the touch, as if branded. But now it was after five on Friday afternoon and the dock was nearly done, would have been done, Brent knew, if someone other than his father had taken the job. They'd have already packed up their saws and drills, gone up to Mr. Hewitt's house to get their check, and be sipping a beer at Macy's Bar and Grill.

However, that wasn't his father's way. The old man had checked everything up top and now waded into the water to confirm that every post was meticulously secured. Only then would he and Brent walk the shore to ensure no wood chips or screws littered the ground. *Even if they never notice, it has to be done right*, his father always said. Which was why, despite Brent's protestations, the old man would hand a client a piece of notebook paper with an itemized cost of materials and labor. If the price was agreed on, his father asked for nothing more than a handshake. Several times the job, once begun, took more materials and labor than anticipated. When that happened, he explained the situation but left it up to the owner to decide on additional compensation. Having worked ten years with his father, Brent was no longer surprised at how often those with the most money balked at paying extra. Such customers also searched intently for some flaw on a completed deck or dock. If they were insistent enough, his father dropped the price a few dollars. Not as much as they'd like but enough to stop their complaining long enough to write the check.

Brent's father waded out of the shallows, the black Maglite held overhead like a torch. He'd rolled his pants above the knees, and in the day's declining light his legs glowed in their paleness. Unlike his muscular arms and shoulders, his legs were thin, each footstep tentative as he waded ashore. Even after a second surgery, the right knee gave way at times, part of the price for countless hours kneeling on wood and concrete.

"Looks good," his father said, so they checked the shoreline and packed the last of their tools into the pickup.

They were glad this job was done. Mr. Hewitt had a reputation for being hard to work for. "A royal pain in the ass," a brick mason had told Brent and his father. Jerry Funderburke, who worked at Lowe's, swore he'd quit the store before going to Hewitt's house again. So Brent and his father had been warned, but since the recession, carpentry work was scarce. Too many days they'd waited at home for the phone to ring, Brent even working part-time at Hardee's to get some extra money. He and Leslie had been talking about having a child, but how could they when the two of them together barely made each month's rent and car loan. But it was Friday, Brent reminded himself. The job was done and they had work for next week already lined up. In a few minutes they would stop at Macy's for a beer before Brent's father dropped him off. If they weren't too tired, maybe he and Leslie could drive to Brevard to rent a movie.

Hewitt was on the lake house's back deck, which was no surprise because he'd been there often during the week. He'd come down to the dock every day. "I'm just wanting to see how far you got," Mr. Hewitt would say, but his eyes always searched for something more. "You're certain those are the right board length?" he'd ask, or "Will those screws hold securely?" They were questions tinged with accusation. Brent's father answered, "Yes sir," but after Hewitt left he'd muttered, "That man knows as much about dock building as a cross-eyed cat."

Mr. Hewitt came down the deck steps with a checkbook in his hand.

"I want to look it over first," he said, and they followed him onto the dock, the boards firm beneath their feet. Farther up the lake a red sun balanced on the hydro dam. A cool breeze swayed the cattails and Brent thought how nice it would be to sit out here with an ice chest of beer as the last jet skis or boats went in. All you'd hear was water sloshing softly against the posts.

"It's a pretty view," his father said, looking out at the lake as well.

"Maybe so," Mr. Hewitt said, "but this railing's too high for the dock to be safe for a child."

"You didn't say you wanted it lower," his father answered. "You didn't say a word about children."

"A professional would think about something like that and consult the client, don't you think?"

His father's face burned as if he'd been slapped, except Brent knew a slap would sting less.

"You were out here yesterday when we began putting it up," Brent said. "You should have said something then."

"I wasn't looking that carefully," Mr. Hewitt answered. "I assumed you knew what you were doing. I'll pay you half of what we agreed on."

The breeze that had bent the cattails ceased. The water stilled as if the lake itself now listened. Brent looked at Mr. Hewitt. What did he know about this man, besides that he was wealthy and from some place where you could make enough money to own a vacation home worth half a million dollars.

"It'll take another day," his father finally said, "but we can lower the railing where you want it."

"And listen to more of the racket your saws and drills have made all week?" Mr. Hewitt answered. "I bought this place for the peace and quiet. No, I'll have it redone sometime when I'm away."

"That's not right," Brent's father said. "We've done good honest work for you."

Mr. Hewitt set the checkbook on the railing, took a pen from his shirt pocket, and wrote out the check. He held it out to Brent's father, who stared at the check as if it was smeared with dog shit.

"This is what I'm paying you," Hewitt said.

"You owe us the full amount," Brent said, "and you're going to pay it."

"Is that a threat?" Hewitt asked. "Look, if you've got a problem with the amount, we can take this to court. But you'd better take the check and be on your way, because if my lawyer gets involved you will end up with nothing."

His father took the check.

"We'll call us a lawyer first thing in the morning," Brent's father said when they got in the truck. "There's got to be some that work on Saturday."

"It won't be worth it, Dad," Brent replied, looking out at the lake. "A lawyer will cost more than what Hewitt owes us, even if we won. Like I've been telling you for months, this is exactly why we need to make out real contracts, to protect ourselves."

"There's lawyers that take a case for a percentage," his father said. "You see them on TV all the time."

"Not for this small an amount."

"There might be one around who'd do it that way," his father said, "just for the principle of the thing."

"It doesn't work that way," Brent said, trying not to sound exasperated. "Why don't we skip Macy's this evening? We'll do it next Friday."

"I don't feel much like stopping to have one myself," his father agreed, then as much to himself as to Brent said, "I don't understand how anyone can act that way and still sleep at night."

They didn't speak again until the pickup pulled into the driveway. Brent got out and took his lunch container and circular saw from the back, then walked over to the driver-side door.

"I'll see you Monday, Dad."

"Why don't you and Leslie come to church Sunday?" his father said. "Folks there have been asking about you all. Afterward you could come to the house for lunch. That would tickle your Mom. Besides, I've been craving banana pudding and she makes it only for you."

"We'll see," Brent said.

Leslie was already home, but he didn't go straight inside. Instead, Brent put the saw and lunch box beside the shed and sat in a swing the previous renters had put up. He'd quit smoking two years ago but he craved one now. *How can anyone act that way?* his father had asked.

Brent had known Ricky Lunsford since first grade. A pale, pudgy boy who carried around an inhaler for his asthma, Ricky had been the kid in elementary school who never got chosen when teams were decided. There had been some teasing, a few times he'd been shoved or tripped, but Ricky never asked a teacher to intervene, and earned a bit of respect for that. He'd retreat to the playground's far corner at recess. In high school Ricky sat alone at lunch. *Just ignore me*, he made clear, *do that and I'll ask no more of you.*

But one day in the eleventh grade, Brent paused at the table where Ricky sat. "You don't need this," Brent said, and took the piece of pizza off Ricky's plate before walking on to where his friends were. Brent did that for two weeks, taking something—pizza, a hamburger, a carton of milk—never a whole plate, which would have been easier. Just one thing. Ricky never tried to stop it. He never said a word. He just let it happen. By the second week, Brent didn't bother to put what he took on his plate. He carried the pilfered food to the nearest trash can and dropped it in.

If a teacher hadn't seen what was happening, how long would he have done it? Not much longer, Brent wanted to believe, but he'd never know for certain because one afternoon the principal called Brent's parents. That evening he and his father went to visit the Lunsfords. Brent had never seen where Ricky lived. It was an old trailer, rust bleeding down the dented tin, concrete blocks rising irregularly to the front door. Inside, it was clean enough, but the furnishings spoke of yard sales and cast-offs. Brent felt remorse but it was his father who apologized to Ricky and his parents first.

"For my son to have done this, I've failed as a parent," Brent's father told the Lunsfords. "Anything I can do to set it right I will. The least we can do is pay two weeks' worth of Ricky's lunches."

His father had taken out his billfold and offered a twenty dollar bill. Mr. Lunsford refused the money, but he and his wife accepted the apology. Mrs. Lunsford had even made light of it, saying it was just boys being boys. Ricky and Brent had shaken hands. There had been no other punishment, but on the ride home Brent's father had said he wouldn't have believed Brent capable of such a thing, words left hanging in the dense silence. Brent still saw Ricky around town but they kept their eyes down if they happened to pass each other.

14

Maybe if he had not been drunk, Brent wouldn't have set the fire. It had happened on the following Tuesday night, the day after his father had given up on any kind of litigation. They were building a deck for a retired dentist from Charlotte. They'd done jobs for the man before and he paid without wrangling over the price, as his father reminded Brent when he insisted they not take another job without a contract that a lawyer had double-checked.

"At least a contract for people we don't know," Brent argued, but his father hadn't replied and Brent knew there was nothing left to say.

That night he and Leslie watched a movie but afterward, when Leslie went to bed, Brent didn't follow. He'd drunk three beers, his usual limit, but he got two more from the refrigerator and went outside to sit in the swing. In a few minutes the bedroom light went off, but the porch and living room lights still shone. Moths swirled around the porch's bare bulb, but the rackety air-conditioner displaced the night's sounds. Six months back, Cam Beecham had offered to sell them this house and two-acre lot, but Beecham was asking a thousand more than the county appraisal. Brent and Leslie had believed he would lower his asking price, but there'd been no new offer.

Brent finished the fifth beer, crumpled the can and tossed it to the ground. He tightened his hands around the bright steel chains, swayed gently back and forth a few moments. When he and Leslie had moved in, Brent had noticed that the grass wasn't worn beneath the swing seat, put up and left as if a taunt. His mind went to the dock and stayed there. Hewitt had been like the mustached bad guy in old-timey movies, except in them the villains got their comeuppance. Brent's father believed a wrongdoer's actions caught up with him eventually. When Brent was growing up, his father would point out how a plumber in Brevard had done shoddy work but then gone out of business, or how a teller at First Citizens embezzled money for three years but ended up in prison. But plenty got away with it, Brent knew. All you had to do was look at the recession that almost caused him and his father to lose everything. The silk-tied Wall Street crooks who'd done it weren't arrested and no one pretended they ever would be.

Brent went to the shed for the gas can and a flashlight. The matches were in the Escort's glove compartment. He didn't switch on the headlights until he'd reached the end of the driveway and turned onto the blacktop. Leslie had the radio tuned to an easy-listening station so Brent stabbed the buttons until something loud and relentless pulsed the speakers.

He pulled off the road at the end of Hewitt's drive and walked down to the lake. The moon and stars were out and he hardly needed the Maglite. All was dark inside the house. Brent soaked the planks and railing with gasoline and stepped back on shore. The first match went out but the second caught. Flames sprinted across the wood. Smoke rose and began obscuring the stars. When Brett got to the car, he saw a bright yellow tongue lapping the water.

The next morning he was in the shower when Sheriff Honeycutt knocked on the door and told Leslie he needed to talk to Brent. Just a matter that needs clearing up, Sheriff Honeycutt answered when Leslie asked why. He waited outside as Brent dressed.

"I called your dad and he's meeting us at the courthouse," the sheriff said when Brent came out on the porch. "Aubrey Hewitt's already there. That dock you built him was set on fire last night."

"And you think I did it?" Brent asked.

The sheriff raised his hand, palm out as he might to halt a car.

"Hewitt thinks it, either you or your father," Honeycutt answered, lowering his hand. "I'd say there's plenty of folks wished they'd done it, including fishermen who bring their boats into that cove. Hewitt calls me and Willie Bost at Fish and Game complaining about them. Like Willie says, the man buys two acres of waterfront and thinks he owns the whole damn lake."

Hewitt and his father waited on separate sides of the courthouse foyer. The room was otherwise vacant, and as the four of them walked across the worn marble to Honeycutt's office, their footsteps echoed.

"All right, Mr. Hewitt," the sheriff said once they were all seated. "Have your say."

"They burned my dock down last night."

"We done no such thing," Brent's father answered.

"Maybe you didn't, as far as being there," Hewitt said, "but your son did and you know he did it. As I told you over the phone, Sheriff, that boy made a threat. 'You're going to pay for doing this to us.' Those were his exact words."

"He didn't say it that way," Brent's father said. "He said..."

But Sheriff Honeycutt raised his hand.

"Let's just deal with who set the dock on fire," he said, and looked at Brent's father, then Brent. "Were either of you near Mr. Hewitt's dock last night, or in a boat on the lake?"

"We don't even own a boat and we weren't around his dock," Brent's father answered. "You've known me long enough to know my word's good, Sheriff. You'll not find me a man in this county who'll tell you otherwise, same for Brent."

"I've never had cause to disbelieve anything you've told me, Dale," Honeycutt said, turning to Hewitt.

"Even if he's telling the truth, that doesn't mean his son is," Hewitt said. "He's the one that threatened me, and I haven't heard him deny anything."

The three men settled their eyes on Brent.

"What do you say, son?" Honeycutt asked.

"I didn't set that fire," he answered. "I didn't even leave my house last night."

"He's lying," Hewitt said.

"If you call me a liar again," Brent said. "I'll give you real cause to hire a damn lawyer."

"There's no cause for talk like that, from either of you," the sheriff said, standing up.

"I'll go up to your place and look around, Mr. Hewitt," Sheriff Honeycutt said, "but unless there's some material evidence that can be tied to these men, there's no cause to charge them. You didn't see anything such as a gas can on the bank, did you?"

"No," Hewitt replied, "but isn't that your job?"

"I just told you I'll look around," Sheriff Honeycutt answered tersely. "We know these men's footprints will be down there, but if someone else's are that might help me find who did this. But my guess is whoever it was came up by boat, probably one of those fishermen you keep harassing. You need to accept that as long as they stay in their boats they can come as close to that dock as they like."

"Talk to them then," Hewitt said. "I gave you and the wildlife officer their boat numbers. Somebody had to have seen something. The way that dock was burning, it looked like the whole lake was on fire."

"I'll check with Fish and Game about any boats that might have been in the cove last night. If not, this isn't likely to get solved." Sheriff Honeycutt paused. "You know, Mr. Hewitt, you'd be doing yourself a favor by being less confrontational with people."

"So," Hewitt bristled. "It's my fault the dock was burned."

"I'm just saying it might prevent something like this from happening again."

"That's good advice the Sheriff's giving you, Mr. Hewitt," Brent said, meeting the man's eyes. "Next time they might set a match to your house."

"There's no need for that kind of talk, son," Brent's father said, but the apprehension now clouding Hewitt's face made Brent think otherwise.

"You do this investigation right, Sheriff," Hewitt said as he stood. "I've got friends in Raleigh, people you're familiar with."

For the first time since he'd picked Brent up, Honeycutt smiled.

"Well then tell them hello for me, Mr. Hewitt."

"Sorry I had to bring you two in," the sheriff said after Hewitt left. "I never believed you all would do something like this, but I had to go through the motions."

"We understand," Brent's father answered.

"You can take Brent home, can't you?" Sheriff Honeycutt asked.

"Of course," his father said, and the two men shook hands.

As they walked out of the courthouse, Brent watched his father's tentative steps, remembered how pale and vulnerable his father's legs had looked last Friday.

They were halfway home before Brent's father spoke.

"That must have been a sight, a dock that long burning," he mused. "There's a lake of fire in the Book of Revelation. Preacher Orr was telling of it just a few weeks ago."

Brent's father paused and gave a slight smile. "Of course, that lake is one you'd not want to be there to see, would you?"

"No sir," Brent answered.

They turned off the main road and soon passed Macy's Bar and Grill. A single pickup was in the driveway, probably left by someone with the good sense to let someone else drive him home. Brent's heart quickened as he thought how easily he might have been pulled over the night before.

"I expect you're feeling it's time for you to go your own way," his father said.

The words were spoken in a matter-of-fact way, neutral in tone. Brent looked at his father's face, but it revealed nothing.

"How so?" Brent asked.

"Business."

"Not you and me," Brent answered, "just the way we do business."

"It's one in the same."

"It doesn't have to be, Dad." Brent said.

"No, for me it does. You're young. You and Leslie want to have a family. I want you to have that too, and a place of your own without fretting each month about whether you can pay the mortgage."

"We can work together," Brent answered. "We just have to change things to make sure we don't get screwed by assholes like Hewitt."

"No, I'll be working only a couple of more years," his father replied, "so I'll stick to my old ways."

"You sure?" Brent asked.

"You're better suited for how things are now," his father answered. "I've known that for a long while."

He glanced over at his father, but the older man looked straight ahead. Soon Brent was thinking of the contract he'd have a lawyer ensure was airtight. Other things would be changed too. He'd cut some corners the way most builders did, jack the price up on material estimates. If he did these things, maybe it wouldn't be too long before he and Leslie did have a child and their own home. His father made the last turn. The swing set came into sight. Almost new, not a speck of rust, as if waiting for a child.

FOUR POEMS
Thomas McCarthy

GUY LOMBARDO

But it begins again when listening to Guy Lombardo
And his Royal Canadians. Out of the depth or height
Of a summer barbecue in Ontario, everywhere I look,
Sunshine follows me as if 'I Don't Want to Walk Without You'
Or 'South of the Border' leads to a kind of July
That turns up the orange glow of a late afternoon.
It's just that a familiar kind of warmth, warm irregular
Stones of your Glenshelane patio, two glasses with
Dried crimson flakes of old sherry, this patio that
Seemed like a small country for making poems, this
Space between me and fragments of shrimp-pink
Petals shearing away from *Violet Carson*, followed by
Great clusters of *Paddy McGredy, Super Star's* vermilion,
The velvet purse of tight *Papa Meilland*, the indecisive
Depth of yellow fringe of pink in *Peace*; it's just that
Something settled in Ontario long ago, a patio as
Small as Ulster, a tiny place with planters or pioneers,
Like the small Protestant note in Irish history that you
Have claimed to hear since childhood. You have heard
It, you said, over and over, and you are as content with
This as any patriot in a foreign jail. For me, it was not
A country or a province, but more an afterglow, as subtle
As the subtle bouquet-garni or the rare essence of
Rose petals; all so like pollen it would make you dizzy.
Because I, like you, must always remain true to my heart
I admit seeing the green and the yolk of Ireland part,
Never to be made whole again, never in all Balmoral
Seasons. Never to declare this is a kind of treason.

I am as odd as be-damned. I am of no historical use
To anyone who doesn't have roses to prune. For my
One true companion I summon up dear Fr. Prout,
That Catholic loyalist in his two-volume *Regina* edition:
Father, it's too late to stop O'Connell. The die is
Cast, and wildly, the way O'Connell's Repealers flung
Fresh vegetables of the Dingle bible colony into the sea
At Inch. What was orange clung to the rocks, wouldn't
Give way. Somewhere a Huguenot called to me from
The depths, from a Canton under the sea. Nobody heard.
But I heard: another kind of history entered my head
With its cracked green shell, its one toppled Omphalos.

GEORGE MORRISON AT AN AOSDÁNA ASSEMBLY

He was not sure about all the others, the ones
Who mark a star for danger with charcoal or acrylic,
The ones for whom a reconstructed shop or attic
Is an art of childhood, or others with the craft
Of manipulating social detail into a form
Of light; or the literary others who take a wide
Walk back into pixelated countryside,
Carrying the can with a pen and a poem –
No, none of that. A long, full life in art
Makes us into priests at the podium,
Longing for the faith we were first promised
When we were alone and young. His part
In the prophecy is perfect; his brief encomium
Spins and spins where cellulose nitrate perished.

AT THE *MONTE CARLO*, MINNEAPOLIS

Peg's *Sidecar* and my *Old Fashioned* settle
In the frosted hour of this early afternoon
Luncheon on a busy Monday in Minneapolis;
Busy for others, that is, the half-serious
Young men who must have come from the
Plush offices of the Wells Fargo Bank, or
Some such institute or Incorporated entity
Where young men find refuge from the very
Things we dealt with, blow by blow, as
Our Twenties' cocktails succumbed to this
Greater need to not be here but to be else-
Where; to be where a guy and a gal
In a story by Scott Fitzgerald might sit and
Contemplate the continuing continuousness
Of America in the late lunch-hour. The usher
Had taken your car and parked it adroitly
In a maze of Minnesota puddles. The waitress
Who might have been the waitress Orson
Welles lied to when he said he needed to step
Outside awhile at Northwestern U., only
To come through a tissue of time and stand
Aghast in Inisheer, or her friend the friend
Who holds a coat or lights a cigarette. As
I was saying, there is always a waitress in
America. There is always a kindly voice to
Interrupt what you were about to say about
That day in this bar in the Twenties when a
Man in a trench coat came in. To our one
Republic, he said, as he took the day's
Takings — and to the hard-working girl, to
This town, and the stories she wished to tell.

THAT PHOTOGRAPH

The distant past is like this analogue tray
In your small red-lit room. On a Greek shore
Where the chemicals are, Bob Dylan is
Singing in the voice he had when you
And I were young, or, well, *younger.* Listen, his
Tall lamp is beautifully timed; the white
Light of our youngest positive hours
Have become blurred, like this quarto image
In a cold tray of fixing fluid. The ascetic
Years rise to greet us. Your deft wrist
Adjusts the tight-lipped aperture. Guitar strings
Of water rise to cleanse this one idea,
This war on time passing that photography is —
Your Venus singing, rising naked from a tray.

The Done Thing, Corporal and Spiritual Works, Bone Rosary, Grievous Love
Thomas Lynch

By getting the dead where they need to go, the living get where they need to be. This seems, after half a century of undertaking, the essential brief, the task most manifest, the raison d'être for a funeral. If these outcomes are not accomplished, whatever else takes place, however pleasant or wretched, meager or sumptuous, is of no real consequence. The accessories amount to nothing—the requiems and mum plants, the shaky brace of pallbearers, coffin plates and monuments, five stages of grief, seven deadly sins, ten commandments, umpteen eschatologies and apostasies—if the essential job's not done, the rest is senseless. To deal with death we must deal with our dead, to get our riddance of the corpse, beloved though it might be, and get ourselves to the edge of the life we will be living without them. And this is coded in our humanity: when one of our kind dies, something has to be done about it, and what that something becomes, with practice and repetition, with modifications and revisions, is the *done thing* by which we make our stand against this stubborn fact of life—we die.

By bearing the dead to their abyss, by going that distance, the living hope to bear the loss of them. By processing the mortal remains we endeavor to process mortality's burdens and heartbreaks. This amalgam of corporal and spiritual works, an effort to deal with the manifest and mysterious life, has been the work that separates humanity from the other animals.

And here some sort of motion, some movement and tasking, some shifting of conditions and circumstance are implicated. Where, the discerning reader will likely wonder, do the dead need to go? Where indeed! And here let me say that what the dead most need, in the moment of their death, is to be gotten, coincident perhaps with hurried and heartfelt farewells, en route to their riddance, their oblivion and abyss, whatever form it takes—the ground, the fire, the sea or air—that elemental disposition which assures they will not embarrass themselves further by putrefaction or decomposition or any of the postmortem indignities that creatures of bone and blood and meat are prone to. And whereas, the Mother of Jesus was assumed into heaven, a feast in mid-August in the Western Church, most of us will find the opened ground or the chambered fire or tomb sufficient to the task of final disposition, a word the etymologist will inform proceeds from dispose, which itself proceeds from the Latin, *disponere* meaning 'arrange,' influenced by *dispositus,* 'arranged' and Old French *poser,* 'to place.' Which is to say we must arrange to place them elsewhere, thus the shoulder and shovel work, the pecking birds that pick the dead thing clean of its rot, the fire, the depths, the tree's high branches: each an end of the done thing somewhere. There are others, we know, but in their final dispositions they are all the same.

I first landed in Clare on 3 February 1970. The inky, oval welcome in my first passport has long since dried; still, I get a glimpse of it again, every time I pass through Shannon or Dublin, as I've done many dozens of times in the intervening years, going half a century now, though we don't feel the time going.

The man in the customs hall in Shannon chalked an X on my bag and waved me on saying, "The name's good." I was twenty-one and possessed of a high number in the Nixon Draft Lotto—a surreal exercise in the existential that had been drawn a couple months before, giving me a pass on becoming fodder for the American misadventure in Vietnam. A lackluster student without goals or direction, I thought I'd better make a move, a gesture to put some distance between my effortless mediocrity at school and my parents' scrutiny. I'd read Yeats and Joyce and reckoned to reconnect with what remained of our family, "On the banks of the River Shannon," as my grandfather had always prayed, over Sunday dinners throughout my youth. His widow, my grandmother, a Dutch Methodist who converted to "The one true faith," as she called the idolatrous superstitions of the crowd she'd married into, still sent Christmas greetings to "Tommy and Nora Lynch, Moveen West, Kilkee, Co. Clare," which is what I told the taxi man in the big Ford idling outside the arrivals hall.

"Can you take me here?" I asked him, proffering the places and names scribbled in my grandmother's sturdy cursive.

I remember Nora Lynch, nearly seventy then, in the doorway of her home, shoulder leaning into the jamb, arms crossed, a study in contemplation, figuring to what use she might put this young Yank on his holidays. Her brother, Tommy, was holding back the snarling dog. I was dressed like a banker's apprentice in my one black suit, polished wingtips and my dead grandfather's watch-fob, trying to make a good first impression, a little hungover from the drinks on the plane and the compression of a night crossing, and despite my efforts, I was as disappointing a Yank as ever showed up in Clare, without property or prospects, cash or complete education. I had Yeats' *Collected Poems* and Joyce's

The Dubliners. They had a newly wallpapered room with a narrow bed and straight-backed chair.

I was their first American cousin to return; they were my Irish connections, twice removed.

"Come in," she said, "you're perished with the journey. Sit in by the fire. We'll make the tea."

Nora and her brother were living on the edge—of Ireland and County Clare to be sure; the north Atlantic just over the road, the Shannon estuary below. Likewise they were, late in their sixties, at the narrowing edge of the lives they'd been given in the opening decade of the twentieth century. First cousins of my late grandfather, to my twenty-one-year-old self they seemed relics of another time entirely, Bruegel-esque, pre-modern, ever, as Yeats claimed, "The indomitable Irishry."

Nora could not have seen her brother's death, of pneumonia, coming round the corner of another year, nor her own long and lonesome vigil by the fire that would come to a close twenty-two years hence. She could not see the trips she would make to Michigan or my many returns to Moveen, nor the family, immediate and extended who would, in the fullness of time, make the trip "home" with me. All of it was the mystery the future always is, rhyming as it does with the history of the past. The moment we're in is a gift, the bromide holds, that's why we call it the "present."

And in that moment, that grey, midwinter Tuesday morning in the yard in Moveen, gift that the present tense of it was, I could not see how it would change my life, to have followed the frayed thread of family connection back to its source and headwaters to this distant townland of Moveen West, a thousand acres divided by families and hedgerows and ditches, the open palm of treeless green pastureland, dotted with shelters and stone sheds, haybarns and outoffices, stretching from high cliffs edging the Atlantic downland to the grey, shingly banks of the Shannon estuary.

In time I would learn all the place names, find the wells and scenic routes, flora and fauna, the mythic and epic accounts of things—how Loop Head was named for the mighty leap the Hound of Ulster, Cúchulainn, made with Mal the Hag in hot and lecherous pursuit of him; how the Montbretia which blooms up the boreens and ditchbanks, coast roads and villagescapes, through July and August leapt over the stone walls of the Vandeleur landlords' walled estate in Kilrush like liberty itself, like water, escaping every effort to keep it in, propagating by mighty nature, a new reality.

The leaps and tributaries of reconnections that I pursued all those years ago were bound to place and people and the ties that bind. In Tommy and Nora I found the last and steadfast remnant of a family sept that had remained while others sailed out of Kappa Pier in Kilrush and Cobh in Cork, a century before a nineteenth-century Thomas

Lynch crossed the Atlantic on a steerage fare and found his way from Clare to Quebec and Montreal, thence to Michigan where he'd heard of a place called Jackson where the largest walled prison in the country was being built and maintained by the unskilled, gainful labor of poor immigrants. "Tom Lynch—Wanted" it read on the tin case he brought his worldly possessions in. He gave that case to his son, who gave it to his son, who gave it years later, now empty, to me.

"Tom that went," said Nora Lynch speaking about the uncle she never knew, handing me a glass of whiskey, "and Tom that would come back. So, now for you." She admired the circularity of time and happenstance. The way what goes around, etcetera.

And nodding by the fire after the welcome and the whiskey and the talk, so brogue-twisted and idiomatically rich, I began to feel the press of hitherto unknown forces—cultural, religious, familial and new—like Dorothy in Oz, I was a long way from Michigan and suddenly and certainly home.

It changed my life, those next three months hunkered over the sods, observing lives lived nearer the essential edge of things, keeping body and soul together, making sense of the elementals, the social and seasonal nuances, the register of imaginative and emotional dynamics, the stories and poems and songs and performances that everyone brought to the evenings' "cúirt"—that gathering of neighbors around hearth and table, each with a party piece, a pound cake, tobacco or drink to add to the evenings' effort to give thanks for another day that was in it. I belonged to a culture of isolates who gathered round our individual, glowing screens to connect with virtual realities. Tommy and Nora lived actual lives on life's terms, which included both the gossip and goodwill of neighbors, come what may. This was a time before country people could escape the contingencies of their geography, before the Fords and Vauxhalls lengthened their range of travel. In 1970 the ties that bind could only be slipped so far as "shank's mare" or the Raleigh bike, the pony trap or ass and cart could take them. They married over the ditch, caroused within the townland or village, got their sacraments within the parish bounds and got their income from their hard labor in their land and the local creamery. That I had come from across an ocean many of their people had crossed and never returned, that I spoke with a Midwest American brogue, that I'd experienced things that were different from them made me momentarily a minor celebrity. But only momentarily. After a while I was just Tommy and Nora's "Yank."

So when Tommy died the following year, in early March of pneumonia, Nora rode her bike into Kilkee to make the call to let me know. When I showed up the following morning to join the wake in progress in Moveen, it upped the ante of our connection. "Most Yanks," a local bromide holds, "wouldn't give ye the steam off their water."

So a Yank who comes running at the news of "trouble," that deftly understated Irishism for a death in the family, seemed to them another thing entirely. But Ireland had taught me things about the ties that bind—the press of family history and place, all the rooted behaviors conditioned over generations.

And when Nora Lynch, in those first months that I spent in West Clare took me to the graveyard at Moyarta, near the banks of the River Shannon in Carrigaholt, it was to the vaulted grave of our common man and the flagstone cut by Mick Troy with the particulars of a sadness eighty years before I ever landed:

Erected by Pat Lynch in memory of his beloved wife, Honor, alias Curry, who died October 3rd 1889 Aged 62 years, may she R.I.P. Amen.

The erector named in the stonecutter's work was Nora Lynch's grandfather, my grandfather's grandfather, thus, my great-great grandfather, thus, our common man. His wife, Honor, for whom the tomb was built, was a grandniece of the Irish philologist and antiquary, Eugene O'Curry, whence, according to Nora, followed any other genius in our gene pool. And it was Pat's wife's slow dying of a stomach cancer that gave him the time, in cahoots with his brother, Tom, to fashion this stone vault at the western side of the burial ground, with the great graven flag stone to cover it, giving the details of his wife's demise and his grievous love for her. He would follow in the fullness of time, as would his son and heir, Simon, Nora's father, as would Nora's twin brother who died in infancy, and finally Nora, her long lonesome vigil quit in March of 1992, her tiny corpse in its wooden coffin lowered into the stone-lined, opened ground to be comingled with the bones and boxes of her ancestors.

They are all dead now, of course, the bed of heaven to them. And I am long since into that age when the wakes begin to outnumber the weddings and we think of ourselves as maybe mortal too. I mostly go for funerals now. Word comes by Facebook or a furtive text or call from the neighbors who look after my interests there—the house, the donkeys, the ones who come and go.

When I got word in June that the poet, Macdara Woods, had died I knew I'd have to make another trip. He was, along with Leland Bardwell, Pearce Hutchinson and Eiléan Ní Chuilleanáin, a founding editor of the Dublin literary journal *Cyphers*. Whereas my poetry had been pretty much ignored in my own country, publication in a Dublin literary journal made me suddenly, internationally unknown. The tiny society of poets who write in the English language would not overfill a minor league sports stadium. More people get chemotherapy every day than read or write poetry. So with some few exceptions, we matter almost entirely to ourselves.

Some years ago, on New Year's Eve, I walked with Seamus Heaney behind the hearse and cortège that took the body of Ireland's most bookish man, the poet, critic, and biographer, Dennis O'Driscoll, from the church in Naas to St. Corban cemetery where he was buried. Nine months later it was Heaney in the hearse and me riding shotgun from Donnybrook in Dublin to Bellaghy in Derry, a three-hour journey into the north to bring the body of the dead poet home, helpless as the few hundred who gathered round the grave, having gone that distance with the great voice of our time because it was all we could do, to be with him who could no longer be among us.

Last October it was a neighbor woman's death by cancer, in June my friend, Macdara Woods, by Parkinson's, then early in August I boarded a plane again in Detroit, making my way to JFK to connect to the late flight to Shannon and thence to Cork City because the poet, Matthew Sweeney, died of motor neuron disease. This year the catalogue of losses seems inexhaustible and I'm thinking it must be the advancing years that put me in the red zone of mortality. In February it was the poet, Philip Casey, who died in Dublin of a cruel cancer; in April my dog, Bill W., long past the eight-year life expectancy of his wooly-mammoth breed, the only mammal over 100 pounds who could bide with me. He was going 13 when his hips and shoulders all gave out. I'd had his grave open for two years plus, fearful of getting caught with a dead dog in the deepening frost of a Michigan winter.

And there's truth in the bromide that by going the distance with our dead, the principle labor of grief gets done, in the deeply human labor of laving the body and laying it out, lifting and lowering, watching and witnessing, having our says and silences. Which is why I'm flying tonight a day late, alas, but nonetheless, to get my friend's body where it needs to go, from Cork City in Munster to Ballyliffin in Ulster, six hours north, where I once caddied for him. I have a hat I bought in the pro shop on the day. I keep it in the clothes press in Moveen and I'll wear it to his obsequies on Wednesday. I've read with Matthew in Dublin, Galway, Cork and Clare; England and Scotland; Adelaide and Melbourne, Australia; Wellington, New Zealand; together we tutored several Arvon Courses at Lumb Bank, Michigan and elsewhere. He's been on trains and boats and planes with me and to each of my principal residences in southeast and northern Michigan and my ancestral stones in County Clare. My heart is fairly desolate these days, with a long-estranged daughter, a long-distant marriage, the low grade ever-present sense of what Michael Hartnett called "the great subtraction". I've been badly subtracted from these last few years. Only for the fact that I banked such friendships against the howling winter of age, that I did not miss the best years of their being and their beloveds' beings and the times of our lives which we caused on purpose to frequently intersect. Two Octobers ago, Matthew made me lamb chops in my own kitchen on the south shore of Mullett Lake where he sat up nights making poems that became the last ones in the last books he published this year. One he called "The Bone Rosary" which was the name I gave to the rope of old soup-bones I'd had the butcher cut from the femurs of cows, and given to my dog, Bill W., to chew the marrow out of. I thought they would make a suitable memorial. The poem ties the dead dog and the dead poet together in my imagination.

THE BONE ROSARY
Matthew Sweeney

The big dog's grave is already dug, a few
yards from the lake, and all the bones he's
sucked the marrow from are strung on a rope
draped over the porch railing, a bone rosary,
waiting to be hooked to a rusty chain hung
from a metal post stuck in the ground, poking
out over the water. I can already imagine
the reactions of people in boats who'll pass,
what they'll think of the resident of the house.
There might be more to tickle their fancy —
I have a BB gun and ball bearings in a cupboard
that would kill as many black squirrels as I
wanted. And I might just commission a black
totem pole. And although there are no records
of anyone walking on the waters of Mullett Lake,
I think I may visit a hypnotist in Harbor Springs
to see if she can facilitate this. I'd love to run out
into the middle of the lake, carrying the Stars
and Stripes and make all the folk in boats
I meet faint and fall into the water, maybe to
drown there, and befriend the big dog's ghost.

My Life as a Painter (Bloodaxe, 2018)

After his burial I came to West Clare where the summer is winding to a close for another year, the last of the holiday-makers are walking the strand line in Kilkee, whale watchers peer through their telescopes at Loop Head, the dolphin boat and charter fishing boat take the last of their passengers out the estuary in Carrigaholt, the pubs are frantic with late-season revelries. The Pope is coming to a nation that has changed religiously in the forty years since the last papal visit. There are worries, after the hot, dry June and July, that there willn't be enough fodder for the coming winter. Round bales of hay and black wrapped silage and heaps of fodder are filling the barnyards, hopes for another cutting abound. Limerick wins the All-Ireland Hurling Championship, a man in the townland succumbs to his cancer; we're passing through life is what is said. We're passing through.

In many places they've lost the knowledge of the done thing and try to reinvent the ritual-wheel every time a death occurs. Dead bodies are dispatched by hired hands, gotten to their oblivions without witness or rubric while the living gather at their convenience for bodiless obsequies where they "celebrate the life," as if the good cry and the good laugh, so common at funerals, had gone out of fashion or lost its meaning. But the formula for dealing with death hasn't changed. It is still essential to deal with our dead; to reconfigure but reaffirm the ties that bind us—the living and dead. It was the Irish connection that convinced me of that.

The reading of poems and sharing remembrances over Matthew's dead body in its box in Cork were good to be a part of, likewise to beckon the mourners to their last look at him, close the coffin lid at the wake the following morning in Ballyliffen at the other end of the island nation which was his home place of the many places he'd called home. He was shouldered from the house and up into the town by family and friends taking their turns at sharing the burden of his remains. Large muscle work prepares the ground of precious memories. It is not the other way around.

I rode in the hearse with Matthew Sweeney's corpse out of town to the grave in Clonmany New Cemetery between showers and the tributes of the couple of hundred fellow humans who stood out in the rain to see the poet's body lowered into ground. It is the done thing here, the only thing that we can do in the maw of rude mortality, the shoulder and shovel work, the words work, wailing, waking, walking and witnessing, the vigil and chit-chat, the holding and beholding these sad duties occasion, the stories we remember before we forget. These ties that truly bind, these sad done things uphold by focusing our diverted intentions on the job at hand, to wit, to get the dead where they need to go and the living where they need to be.

August Kleinzahler

Before Winter, Part II

Peaches on top of the compost, sitting pretty
rot from underneath blue
jays swoop
down for poppyseed then curl
back up to the fencepost
quick
on account of cat, he's
got a lot of tricks, funny
angles and spots
he'll jump out at you from

if a peach hasn't brained him yet
the way the fool
sleeps chin to dirt right under-
neath the damn tree's big fat peaches too hard
and no good to eat, rotting
from the bottom up, nematodes
sowbugs, larvae, mites & spores slaphappy
feasting on sugar

cook the heap of pith, stalk and leaf
so cat'll sleep warm
between rosemary and nasturtium
sipping nitrogen
at its base hoping mice or crickets or
some kind of electric
shifts an ion in his whisker
opening one eye as snails both sides
of him, above and below

lay their trails down in the night

HOW TO PASS
Louise Crimmins Piantedosi

1st Prize, Seán Ó'Faoláin International Short Story Competition

Now and then, remember what Spinelli said: *Jane Reardon. Great name. So Town and country.* Thank the practical ancestor ambitious enough to drop the O or the Mc. Thank Bowdoin, where you lost your neighborhood accent for something vaguely upper crust. Be grateful you observed so many crusty ways. You can blunt cut and kitten heel your way through any door in Boston. At least you think so. But then again. *Spinelli.* What the hell would he know?

Keep things professional. Never personal. No need to mention that your town was a Hyde Park duplex, that your country was a Wilmington split level ranch. Briefly wonder: how could your parents not have seen it? Every house they chose to live in had been halved. Lose yourself in your work. Stay at the office late. Resist the urge to share that you, too, have a family connection to the firm: don't risk being pressed for details. But when the cleaning woman comes around to feather dust and empty out your trash, think of Nora, the grandmother you never met. Most likely, Nora averted the eyes of the stay-laters, too. Think about feather dust and all the zillions of used-to-be-birds.

Make yourself useful. Volunteer. Kerry for Senator! Teresa Heinz Kerry is kind to you. You're her fledgling. Her little sparrow in a box. You suspect she knows an outsider when she sees one: she won't give you away. Her accent is Mozambiquan. She speaks conspiratorially. She winks at you when she talks. She gives you plum assignments: you're the fresh face for the campaign, you're the volunteer in the photo shoot, you're the airport greeter of Bon Jovi, you personally deliver the hat Governor Weld left behind. Don't tell her you felt offended by her husband, who looked right past you to find the more important people in the room. But because she's a noticer, Teresa notices you noticing. She tells you of his having been Mr. Vietnam Vets Against the War. She knows how to keep you in the camp. Continue to assist at her small parties. Learn ever crustier ways: the value of the proper canapé, that gin should be London dry, that everyone loves a layer of bacon, that—even in summer—men's shirtsleeves must *never* be short.

Someday you'll use her idea of having a portrait artist in the room. You cherish the sketch the artist did of you. You tape it to your wall. And you will always remember Teresa's kindness, especially when you order fries.

Don't forget your limits. You don't have to quit because your boss suggests team tennis but be ready with a good excuse. An unhealed fracture or intermittent vertigo will do. Stay in your comfort zone. Become a member of the Museum of Fine Arts or the Athenaeum Library instead.

Resist sarcasm. Suppress proletarianism. Deny yourself the urge to yank the string of pearls from Sally Usher's neck. *Oh no dear, you can't buy them for yourself. They're like opals. They must be gifted!* Don't ask if Sally's gifting grandmother ever heard of the Ama, the Japanese women who free-dove deep for them, knives roped to naked waists, each pearl a breath held for minutes. Don't ask if Sally realizes how many centuries of people have suffered for shit that her kind *must* possess. And don't ask if the new bond fund brochure is being printed at a union shop. Definitely don't do that. But if you do slip up at, say, a party, pretend it's just the drink. No matter that you're sober. You know the speechisms of drunkism. Let someone gallantly send you home in a cab so you won't need to drive on the eshkshresh. Ekshpresh. Expreshway.

Ignore people from your past, no matter how significant. Better yet, have no past. Be Gatsby, minus the house, the parties, the Daisy, and the crime. But if you do happen upon, for example, your father, whom you've had no contact with for the ten years since your mother, thank god, threw him out of the house, just keep walking with your colleagues to Quincy Market happy hour. Or, if you must, tell them you've forgotten your keys at the office and circle back. Even if your colleagues, for some reason, turn around, they'll never guess the identity of the cabbie at the taxi stand waiting for a fare. Be as kind as you can. Don't let on you've ignored him before, the rumpled man in the ironed suit, how you've watched from a distance as he put down his sample case and sighed. Instead say, *Hi. Dad? I thought that might have been you.* His face is red. His hair is white. His sleeves are short. He says it's good to see you doing so well. He says he's never loved a job better. The people he meets. The freedom he has. Someday he'll tell you about the back roads to Logan. He stares at your Kerry-for-Senate button. *Hmmph. You're voting for that phony? Lousy tipper,* he says. Don't tell him where you work. Don't tell him where you live. Say goodbye, good to see you and walk away. Briefly hyperventilate. Don't panic. Your sea wall has been breached, but it's not irreparable. Resolve to never hail a cab. Skip happy hour and just go home instead.

Refocus on your work. Be enthusiastic about your boss's commands. *Jane, I want you to let loose. Write something radical,* he says from above his bow tie and behind his wire rims. Radical? About bond funds? He's looking at your kitten heels. Meow. You've got this. You're known for writing with punch. It doesn't take you long. *Workers of the world, delight! N* tie, bow tie. *Beacon Hill, Bunker Hill. Name stitched on a uniform, name etched on a silver spoon. Fidelity has a product for you! Thanks to our expert management, broad diversification, and low minimums, anyone can invest like the rich do now.* Your boss is silent for a bit. *Um, I think you took my use of the word radical too literally, Jane. You know what I'm going to say. Back to the drawing board.* Take this literally, too. Go back to your desk and doodle. Always either a face like yours or a flower in a pot. Wonder if, instead of English and American history, you should have majored in art.

Cheer up. Appreciate the view. You're on the 23rd floor, cubicled beside the one flank of glass wall not blocked by executive suites. You overlook the harbor! Contemplate the history: you're on *the hill* of the City Upon a Hill speech, the speech poached by Reagan and JFK, the one by Governor Winthrop of the lobby portrait, of the silly frilly collar, of the long hands and long face—a face as long as his descendant John Kerry's. From this vantage point, it's easy to see who's at the bottom of that hill, and who's at the top. Wonder what the hill was like before these buildings were buildings. Think about Samoset. Think about Squanto. Now there's a guy who must have had regrets.

Don't respond to that cafeteria bulletin board notice for an apartment in South Boston, even though it seems to have been posted just for you. It pulsates. It sparkles. It smells like a rose. It *psssssssts* and *hey yous* until you rip it from its tack when no one else is looking. Exposed brick. Hardwood floors. Walking distance to the T. Reasonable rent. Be forewarned that the move will fissure you. And if you do move, don't give HR your new address. Mail can be forwarded forever! Survey the prospective neighborhood from your lofty post. Notice that it's guarded by a rusting hulking bridge that you'll call Cerberus, that it's moated by dark waters, a tiny huddled kingdom tipsy, tough, and bleak. Never mind that the one St. Patrick's Day parade you saw there scared you. Break your old lease. Sign the new lease. Even your best friend will say, *Really? There? A racist neighborhood like that?*

But trust your gut. Consult your higher self. Reread Joseph Campbell. You're being drawn here for a reason. Invisible pipes, the pipes, are calling you. Your first week there, you'll hear a real tin whistle and try to find its source, only to be distracted by the waves at Carson's Beach. Many years from now, you'll learn your grandfather, youngest of thirteen, was born right here, on the very street where you decide to live. You'll be outraged that not one person in the family ever thought to mention this to you, even when you wondered why *this* was the one and only neighborhood that leaving made you cry.

Observe their ways, this new tribe to which you are at least ethnically connected. Avoid faux pas. For panhandlers, always carry quarters and ones. Especially when at the Broadway Station waiting for the City Point bus. Regret you didn't share your little joke about being glad to learn the city has a point. Don't repeat the mistake you made with Murphy, whom you mistook for a random bum. When you instinctively recoiled, he unsmiled and said, *Do I really look that bad?* He waited for an answer. His hair was wild and red. The wind was strong. You finally chose the tough love answer. *Yeah. You do. You really do.* You felt instant regret. You felt oxymoronic. Like tough love. Which you always believed was a myth. You noticed people gave each other the side eye. Someone patted him on the back. Someone gave him a ten. You realized they all know him. That here, there's no such thing as a random bum.

Continue to develop strategies. Join a gym just so you can doff your Burberry on your way home from work. Stuff it in a duffel. Put on a pea coat. Slip into Keds. Go alone to see Sinéad O'Connor at the Paradise. When she sings a song in Irish, feel the shatter of internal glass. Consider shaving your head. Consider Doc Martens. Feel guilty about being the harbinger of gentrification your neighbors know you are. Don't expect a hello back.

Don't even try to pretend you can't hear your boss calling out to you from across the office floor. Everyone knows it's the kind of call they'll find you for. It has crackle and heat. It cuts through dimensions. It's the kind no one wants to get, the one from a relative who goes through the switchboard, who makes the receptionist find your boss. *Jane. Your Aunt Rose O'Malley is on the line. It's about your father.* Feel as if you should put your hands up, feel as if you must cough up feathers before your extension rings and you pick up the phone.

Go to the hospital. Go out of duty. Go out of curiosity. Go because who else is there but you. The hospital is a busy little city where everyone knows where they're going except for you. Find the ICU. There he is. I see you. He says, *Hah!* Like someone who's embarrassed to be photographed. His hair day is bad. His feet are bare. The blanket is short. Johnny wearing a johnnie, pale blue with tiny white dots: who wouldn't be embarrassed by that? He's immobilized. He's attached to multiple translucent tubes. He's a fly alive inside a web. You share this observation later with your mother on the phone. *I'll bet it's a tangled web. That man was a deceiver!* she says. *Now he'll know what it's like to be stuck all day in one goddamned place.* A year ago, she moved to the hills of North Carolina. She's awaiting the Rapture. Her car has four-wheel drive. Pull the blanket over your father's feet. He says if he hadn't broken his ankle, they wouldn't have looked at his heart. Can't get over it. How lucky is that? You say, *Somebody's looking out for you. Luck of the Irish, right?*

He gives you the keys to his Malden apartment. He lets you borrow his car. He needs you to grab some clothing. Something more than the khakis. More than the sweatshirt that's encrusted with tomato seeds from the BLT he was holding when he tripped over the footrest of the recliner. His apartment building is yellow brick with stone scrolls carved above the entry. It's surrounded by maples. It used to be grand. The hallway smells like dust and radiator steam and the heavy dark wood of the doors. Each door has a window of rippled glass. Each looks like a detective agency door. You feel like a detective. You feel like a spy. You open the door to a room flooded with afternoon sun. Surprise! You see a flower box in every window. They're planted with petunias. They wink a welcome at you. They're abundant. They've been deadheaded. Their pink looks neon in this light.

Every surface is stacked with newspapers and books. They're covered in invisible moss. You find boxes of Polaroids. And pictures from Kodak Instamatics. They're almost all taken from the window of a car. You slowly come to recognition. You see the Hyde Park duplex. You see the Wilmington split ranch. These are shots of every place you've ever lived. You see the Brookline Village storefront where you worked before Fidelity. You see the apartment where you lived with your brother and your mom. You see your own apartments, including the one where you live now. He's been a living ghost. He's been a drive-by haunter. You find a birthday card from someone named Cookie. Close the box, grab the clothes, water the plants.

Three weeks later, he visits you in South Boston. He's small at the bottom of the stairs, still hobbled by his cast. But his lease on life is new. For a moment, you see Johnny the child, and it makes you sad. Aunt Rose told him your car has been troubled. It keeps stalling out. *Sounds like the alternator. Easy fix,* he says. Together you walk into the unswept street, the bright unshaded sun. Men are out walking. Probably toward Castle Island. Where the breeze is the sea. Where they all go out walking. Red-faced. White-haired. Short-sleeved. You pop the hood of your car. Neighborhood boys show up to help you. They see the Kerry bumper sticker on your car. *That guy's a phony. His family name's not really even Kerry. Pretendin' to be Irish to get our vote and shit.* They're proud their vote is wanted. And they all know how to fix a car.

FIND YOURSELF HERE
R.S. Wynn

2nd Prize, Seán Ó'Faoláin International Short Story Competition

Slinging wheatgrass shots and collagen smoothies at the Jamba Juice on the corner of 4th Street and Santa Monica Boulevard was not in my five-year plan when I moved from New Hampshire to California—but here I am. It's 6:15 a.m. on a Tuesday in June. The twenty-fifth consecutive Tuesday I've opened despite having been hired as a closer. Rising before the sun, I showered with baby wipes and coconut body spray, caked my eyelashes with mascara, and shimmied back into the wrinkled khakis and brown apron I'd left heaped on the floor. At least the dingy uniform hides the monochrome watercolor I've painted down my tits with coffee stains.

When I drove south on the PCH this morning, fog still had a chokehold on the beach. They call it "June Gloom," this vapor wall redolent of fish shit and motor oil that refuses to burn off until early afternoon. Groggy seagulls loiter on the sand, almost invisible, pecking at lemon peels and straw wrappers—detritus from a human tide. I'd like to loiter too, wait until the horizon flatlines and watch disappointed surfers paddle their boards ashore, but instead I'm here. The store is ready and I'm in position behind the counter, between the cast iron Sundance Wheateena Workhorse II juicer and our purportedly "whisper silent" array of blenders. Seconds from now, the blenders will be humming, mashing the delicate architecture of fruits and vegetables into a baby food goo for grownups too busy to chew.

Sure enough, the door swings open at 7 a.m., ringing the shopkeeper's bell recently installed by Mrs. Yu, our zealous franchise owner. It'll ring in here like a call center for the next hour or two. First, a wave of early bird fitness addicts will stop to chug their liquid breakfasts after hitting the gym. Then the office zombies will descend, operating under the belief that consuming 500-calorie Kale-ribbean Breeze smoothies every morning will help them discover their inner beach bodies.

My co-workers, Josh and Bonnie, snap to attention when they hear the bell. Stuck over by the register, Josh is like a hummingbird in a shoebox. Pumped after rising for a 4 a.m. surf, Josh opens the store Wednesday through Saturday and has managed to memorize half our regulars' names. He chats them up whether we're slammed or slow. *Angie, how's the new job treating you? Becca, back from Penn State already? Charles, my man, how're your grandkids doing?* A born farm boy, Josh migrated from Ohio hoping to model. In the meantime, he coasts by on native charm and discounted shakes. Nothing but groovy vibes for everyone.

Bonnie is too good for this world, at least that's what Mrs. Yu always says. *Bonnie, you cleaned out the freezer before I asked? You're an angel, just too good for this world.* Bonnie is one of those girls who wants everyone's love and knows exactly how to get it.

Yesterday, a manicured stay-at-home mom came in with three pig-tailed girls in matching outfits, all squealing their orders in unison. A Greek chorus of consumerism. Bonnie was gentle but firm with the girls. "Sweeties, if you order one at a time with your inside voices, I'll give you extra sherbet." Then she cooed to their mother, "They're so adorable! I hope I have three just like them."

Minutes later, a bodybuilder came over to the counter swinging a Cadillac keychain. He tapped the fob in mock thoughtfulness against the freezer glass in case anyone in the joint hadn't noticed him and his enormous Escalade. Bonnie swiftly inched her polo down so the black lace of her bra poked out from the plain khaki weave.

"I recommend the Peach Pleasure," she said arching her back as she gestured to the smoothie menu overhead. "I just love peaches, you know what I mean?"

At least Bonnie knows what she wants, and she lands her conquests with the confidence and flare of a gymnast's salute. What was *my* plan when I moved out here after college, $80,000 in debt, nothing but my BA in Classical Literature in hand? I thought I'd disembark my plane and stumble into a B-film Grace Kelly story: small town girl gets the hell out of Nowhere, New Hampshire; goes to Somewhere, California; becomes Somebody. I fell for the Travel and Tourism Commission's slogan: "California—Find Yourself Here." Turns out, that cross-your-fingers-and-hold-onto-your-tits type of plan might fly at twenty-two, especially if you're 5'10", blonde, and independently wealthy. I'm closing in on twenty-six, an inch shy of 5'2", and too broke to buy the beverages I serve, even with the employee discount. Still, I've only been in California for a few years. Josh has been here for five and has yet to land a single modeling gig. He hasn't lost faith.

"Um, like, hello?" An impatient, emaciated cherub interrupts my flow with her flawless Valleyspeak, straight from the bowed lips of Alicia Silverstone circa *Clueless*. Only this girl's maybe nine years old, wearing an Adidas tracksuit and UGGs, and peering on tiptoes into the freezer on my left. She's waited long enough that she's rubbed her nose grease all over the freezer window. The glass looks like an impromptu tic-tac-toe board. She continues to smudge her face left and right, trying to get a better view of our frozen treats—if you count fruit as a treat, which they do around here.

"So, like, how many calories are there in a strawberry?" she asks. The girl's mother, head to toe in sea-breeze blue Lululemon, hovers behind her.

Interactions like this are foghorns calling through the gloom. Opportunities to dust off my Grace Kelly fantasy and set something right in the world. OK, maybe not Grace Kelly, but with a little practice and I might be the next Tina Fey.

"OMG," I exclaim, flipping my unflattering brown hair over my shoulder. "Strawberries have, like, mega calories. They're disgusting. *But—*" a pause here to pique their interest before I resume with vocal fry and high-rising terminals, "science people have discovered that strawberry seeds are loaded with post-Hellenic cathartics. These HCs, as they're called, are randomized by dramatic peripeteias in the lower intestine. So, as long as you eat the *seeds*, strawberries are like basically calorie-free."

The daughter is skeptical. Kids tend to be incredulous around that age, soon after the Santa Claus lie has been revealed to them. The mother, however, who probably hasn't tasted fructose in years, is desperate to believe my bullshit propaganda.

"Seriously," I say, looking the spandex-clad mom dead in the eye. "I read it on Wikipedia."

Moments later, Josh rings them up for two 450-calorie Strawberry Surf Rider smoothies. The mom strokes her daughter's hair as they leave, forgetting all the grown-up fear and ambition she's hoisted onto her daughter's slight frame. This might not be what I planned, but I swear, I'm doing god's work out here.

Sometimes, though, when I'm elbow deep in a freezer, struggling to scrape the last bite of sherbet from a container so Mrs. Yu won't lecture me about her bottom line, I think about prostituting myself. I read an article in *The Atlantic* about young Ivy League women pimping themselves out on sugar daddy websites like some modern Moll Flanders. Fingers sticky from sherbet, I formulate my own plan: *all I'd have to do is bleach my hair and hit a yoga class once a week.* I think: *If I auctioned myself online, I'd only have to work a few days a month.* Rent, paid. Car loan, paid. Student loan, paid. Utilities, paid. Maybe I'm overvaluing my sexual worth. Still, I bet I'd be able to save up to buy a house someday. Not in Santa Monica. Anywhere in northern Arizona though. Fort Defiance. Bitter Springs. Maybe Casa Grande.

Child, a salty voice in my head interjects. *You cannot put a price tag on your self-respect.* The voice sounds distinctly like my mother's. I'm inclined to ignore it. On my commute this morning, some pundit on KCRW was yammering about upwards social mobility, saying it's positively correlated with higher education. A dressed-up version of my mom's customary speech: *Get up. Get out. Go get a degree.* Four years of state college later and all I see is a mortgage payment worth of college debt disappear from my account each month, just like it will for the next twenty years. Doesn't matter what I do, I can't live out my mother's dreams.

I know working at a Jamba Juice a breath away from the Pacific Ocean in a state with one of the world's largest economies isn't exactly *The Jungle*. Still, you can't convince me this isn't debt bondage. Mrs. Yu tells me when to wake up, what to wear, and where to stand. She puts words in my mouth, this fucking script I repeat a thousand times a day to upsell for her. *Would you like an Açaí Primo Bowl with that? Tired? Have you tried scorching your esophagus with a ginger shot?* I clang on and on like that stupid bell stuck inside the door. After a 50-hour week of servicing strangers for a nickel above minimum wage, you can't convince me I'm not selling my time, my body, my life—and selling them cheap. *But hey,* I tell the mom-voice in my head, *I'm broke, and I need the money.*

"Hey, uh, what *is* wheatgrass?" Suddenly I notice the man staring at me, cow-eyed, across the top of the juicer where we grow wheatgrass for our signature coolant-green shots. This guy is so chiseled and tanned—he's Myron's Discobolus. He's a Calvin Klein mannequin.

My gaze shifts down to the blades of wheatgrass reaching up between us, waving in the AC like the hands of eager students certain they can answer his question.

"Well, it's *wheat* and it's *grass*. Wheat-grass."

"Like *grass* grass?" he asks, wrinkling his narrow nose. In truth, at $3 per ounce I'm sympathetic to his dismay, but it's almost 10 a.m. and I'm in desperate need of my ten-minute break. I default to Mrs. Yu's script.

"Wheatgrass is rich in vitamins and minerals, it contains amino acids, enzymes and chlorophyll—like most grasses." Here I lean in. "We just don't extract the juice of most grasses because it's disgusting."

"Hit me up," he says, undeterred, folding his arms across his chest. He sticks his hands deep into his armpits, rubbing his sculpted pecs with his thumbs while he watches me and waits.

Knife out, I cut a fistful of the grass from the lawn on top of the Wheateena Workhorse. The blade releases a fragrance reminiscent of my early summers spent in New Hampshire. Back then I'd never seen an ocean, but rivers of clear, cold water flowed down from the Franconia Range and babbled in small brooks behind my childhood home. I used to lie on a blanket on the fresh-cut grass of our yard and inhale the vivid, sugary scent of clover flowers. Summer after summer, I searched for a four-leaf clover, my fingertips stained green as I poked through bleeding blades of grass. Never flagging. Never flinching. Never doubting that my hard work would ultimately equal good fortune.

Maybe that's why I hate California, the land of eternal believers. The people here are always ready to try the next fad diet or power cleanse, to believe they're one nip/tuck away from bliss, one bilious shot from inner and outer peace. Even the Jamba Juice slogan, "Blended for the BEST YOU"—they buy it. They're so certain that if they keep digging, sifting, purging, cutting, sifting, they'll strike it rich. Josh and Bonnie, Mrs. Yu, our customers: they're all moving toward greater faith. I wasn't any different when I came out here, but somewhere along the way I fell out of the race. I've turned dirt upon piles of dirt and nothing glitters anymore. All I see are hungry people chewing the cud of a hungry Earth.

I hand the frothy green shot over to the human sculpture. His neck veins bulge as he tries, but fails, to toss the liquid straight down the back of his throat. He gags, shivers, and runs his bright green tongue over his bright green teeth.

"Nasty," he announces and pushes the empty cup back towards me. "Throw that out for me. I'm going to pretend this never happened." He walks out the door and turns toward the ocean.

The fog is burning off. Blasts of desert heat push into the store with the late-morning wave of customers. They are the jet-lagged. The tourists. They've come to ride the Pacific Park Ferris Wheel on the Santa Monica pier, then maybe drift down toward Venice Beach. They talk about how nice life would be if they lived here. Maybe here they'd be discovered. Maybe they'd get famous. Be valued. Loved. In their five-year plans they never imagine becoming me. Above their banter I hear the shopkeeper's bell ring and ring, growing louder. Incessant. It speaks to me, chiming each time the door closes: *you're nothing, you're nothing, you're nothing, you're nothing.*

Heading north on the PCH after my shift, the radio hums a monotone between stations. It's 3 p.m. and I'm doing 20 in a 45, cars on every side of me. We rattle around each other like empty bottles battering the pier at high tide. We bob on waves of pavement like surfers waiting for some greater force—a god-stroke—to push us in a clear direction.

The cars around me have their windows rolled up; I guess their ACs work. Windows down, I breathe their exhaust. Sweat drips from my throat, courses hidden streams under my tits. Tickles my stomach. There's a pocket knife in the glove compartment; I could slice through the knot yoking my apron to my neck. I could tear off my polo and my khakis too, shred my whole kit to ribbons and toss it out the car's window. It'd flutter through the air like a seagull released from a cage: dirty and brown, flapping and falling by the road outside Malibu. The wind would kick my uniform down that razor strip of beach until it slipped into the ocean and disappeared—like none of this ever happened.

Maybe then I'd keep driving, buck-ass-naked all the way up to Leggett in Mendocino County to see the redwoods. Imagine that: the wind spilling all around me like I'm a baby again, naked on our white clover yard in Franconia. I'd drive through the night, cool air teasing goosebumps across my thighs, rippling my skin the way rain marks the sand. The fog will roll in at dawn, painting my breasts with floating pearls of rain, combing star-fields of dew through my hair. Does it matter that I can't find myself here? Would I care if I could leave this place to the people who know how to live in it, people like Josh and Bonnie who can dream on their feet? Maybe I really would keep driving too, if I had more than half a tank of gas and twenty bucks until payday.

Coming around Mugu Rock, the traffic slows inexplicably, then stops. Along the beach, seagulls are heaving their bodies against the Santa Ana winds. They jump onto each other's backs, desperately vault into the air with the ragged wings of plastic bags swirling around them, but the wind churns it all up and hurls them backwards across the beach. The seagulls leap again and again, hoping to catch an upwards drift. Maybe one gull in a hundred will succeed; it'll bound at just the right moment and just the right angle and find itself midair, free. But the rest—I wonder how many times they'll try and how far back they'll be blown? How long can they push against oblivion?

SOMEONE ELSE'S PROBLEM
Kevin Connelly

At Portadown the soldiers, he knew straight away, were going to check him out. Slowly they walked down the aisle towards him. No-one pointed at him or gestured towards him, but he knew he would be the one. Rifles pointed down, trigger finger at the ready, he noted, they continued their measured advance.

"Name!" The voice was not too loud but there was no mistaking the underlying firmness.

He gave his name, reaching into the top pocket of his jacket for photographic ID. He handed it over, wondering if his warmest winter jacket might somehow be wrong in the eyes of the soldiers. The ID was held, examined, passed behind.

"Where are you going?"

In response he rooted in another pocket and pulled out a letter she had written in the autumn. There was a return address on the envelope. He showed him that. The soldier turned it over, read his name and address. Bored now he passed it behind him and made to move on.

"Check that matches the ID," the soldier said.

The second soldier looked at the ID, looked at the envelope, turned it over, looked at the sender's address, and finally looked at him. He just grunted, handed back the letter and the ID, moved on. The rest of them stared hard at him as they passed by.

He was annoyed while being at the same time, somehow relieved. All he wanted was to see her, to take a break. He could have a few good nights while the money lasted. She had said, "You can see me anytime, don't fret. We'll find a place for you to stay."

Now here he was, on the train going north, taking her at her word. He had written but heard nothing in reply. There was, he thought, a good chance she hadn't received it yet. A few days previous there had been no thoughts of doing anything like this. A seldom-seen uncle passing through on his way to the ferry had been met at the docks. They'd had a good chat, he'd enjoyed himself and as he made to go his uncle said, "Here, take this, I'd say you could find a good use for it."

With a smile and a wave from his aunt they were gone, and he was left holding in his hand enough for a return ticket to Belfast and the chance not to be deeply broke, for a few days at least.

The train moved swiftly along. Soon he would be at the station, changing to a bus. What seemed to his eyes to be densely packed housing rolled by, interlaced by roads heavy with traffic. He relaxed further into his seat. Where roads crossed over the railway line the carriage momentarily darkened and he caught glimpses of his reflection. He felt that he looked good. He smiled and drifted into thoughts of meeting her, of what might be. They had never gone as far as he wanted. She loved him, she said, as a friend, a very close and special friend. She didn't want to spoil that. Who knows, he thought, who knows how it might go?

"Ah son, you shouldn't be here at all!" The woman's voice sounded tired, the Northern tones resigned.

"You shouldn't be here at all," she repeated, looking around as if to locate where he should be and how to get there.

He too had looked around immediately after he stepped off the bus. He was in a wide-open space by the side of the main road. Behind him, rising up the hill, were rows and rows of almost identical looking housing.

There wasn't a tree or a bush or a park bench anywhere in the green area. Everything from the housing down to the main road was open and exposed. There were just acres of close-mown grass, edged by the first of the streets and fringed by the skeleton of a burnt-out bus and the rusted hulks of a few cars.

Just like the woman, he had known straight away he shouldn't be there at all. He had cursed himself immediately for his wrong choice of bus stop. Springhill, Springmartin, Springfield, Springburn? He had made the wrong choice, clear straight away when every streak of graffiti told him so. The Pope was well and truly fucked if he ever got here and so was he if he didn't get out.

Walking along the path, staying close to the main road, avoiding a group of men around black taxis a few hundred yards away, he had decided to ask the first old lady he met. If he walked towards the next bus stop, a good distance away, he would get further away from the taxis, figure out something.

The woman at the bus stop looked at him again and with pity in her voice said, "For your life son, don't ask that question and you around here."

He mumbled thanks, more conscious of his accent than he had ever been.

"Go you up to yon crossing over the road up there." She pursed her lips, thought a bit and continued, "I'm not right sure of the street you're looking for, but," she hesitated, "I'm fair sure someone over there will be able to help you."

He thanked her, relieved that his instincts had been right, that an elderly woman on her own might look kindly upon a wayfaring stranger, hoping someone else might do the same for one of hers someday.

As he headed towards the crossing she called quietly after him, "Mind how you go and be careful who you open your mouth to around here."

"You shouldn't be here at all." The doorway was a neat frame for the man, large and bulky, eyeing the young stranger closely. He grinned suddenly, "Och, no son, she's down by the College now, living in a house wi' some of her friends. Annie!" he shouted over his shoulder, "Call out her new address there, will you?"

He wrote down the address the man gave him on the envelope. He asked for detailed instructions for the bus changes he needed to get there. A girl, younger than him and mad with curiosity about the young man who had come so far to see her sister, told him what he needed to know.

"Come on," she added, "I'll walk you to the bus stop."

She tried to pump him for gossip. Where did they meet? What brought him up here? Was she in trouble? He had younger sisters himself and was easily able to divert her. As he jumped on the correct bus she yelled after him as a parting shot, "Tell her I've got her room now, she needn't mind coming back!"

This time, no bother, he followed the directions he was given and ended up at the right address, an older, quieter district. Mature trees could be seen at the end of the street. A giant yellow crane was bright and cheerful against a sky turning to blue beyond the park. There was no-one in.

He went to the pub on the corner. After a pint and a ham sandwich with mustard relish he began to feel better. The pint tasted strange, sharper where he was used to a smoother, creamier drink. It was a relief that his accent was not a problem. If anything, it broke the ice. Afternoon drinkers, long bored with each other's company, were delighted to have a youngster, not from thereabouts, to exchange banter with.

Then she was there. Suddenly, unexpectedly there and he thought, exactly as before, that she was beautiful. He laughed easily, she smiled, and her smile, on her lips and in her eyes, was as bright as the sunlight now streaming through the nicotine-stained windows.

"I only looked in to see if Marie was there, you'll meet her. I don't always do that, but I felt like I should look in today." She linked her arm through his and glanced at him repeatedly as she spoke.

At the door she stopped and looked at him closely and said again, "I can't believe it! You just came up and managed to find me here." She sounded glad; she threw her arms around him and hugged him tightly. For a time, he lost himself in her embrace and was conscious of nothing but the softness of her long red hair against his cheek. He breathed deeply, inhaling her scents, shampoo, perfume. They clung to each other comfortably until she said, "There now, come on and we'll get you inside."

After a flurry of introductions in the kitchen, none of which he caught properly, they were alone again in a bedroom upstairs.

"You can leave your bag there," she pointed to a bare space on the floor. The room was cramped; two beds jammed together with little space between them dominated the room. Leaning against the fragile-seeming wardrobe, he pulled aside the net curtain for a clearer view.

An untidy garden backed onto its twin. The green between the houses softened the monotony of red brick. It reminded him of where he had left to be here.

He wondered where exactly he would end up sleeping. As if prompted by a subtle telepathy she faintly blushed, a pale pink flush faintly colouring her pale skin. Almost shyly she said, "Come on, I'll show you where you can freshen up. Lord! I still can't believe you made it here, and you found me."

He trailed along the corridor behind her as she led the way to a bathroom which looked as though it hadn't been maintained in about forty years. Alone and catching sight of his reflection again, he felt suddenly nervous, unsure. What if this didn't work out? Didn't go the way he hoped, planned? Throwing the towel on the basket he shrugged at himself in the mirror and stepped back outside. She was there again.

"Ready?" Her smile was enough for him. "We'll go into town, just the pair of us. We can get something to eat and then," she almost leaned on the word, "then we'll go somewhere for a few drinks, you'll meet loads of people."

Feeling like he had done that already, he felt in lighter mood all the same. He took her arm in his, smiled at her and said, "In that event, it's time we left."

"See? I told you, life goes on." Her hand across the table lay on his. His distress was clear to her. With sympathetic eyes she continued, "Don't think about it. I know it's strange, but there you are. What else do you do?"

What else could he do? He enjoyed the meal they shared, the easy way they felt together. Over the candlelight her eyes sparkled in the beautiful restaurant built out of the ruins of the bombing. He loved the light reflected in the shining curves of her hair. She caught the look in his eyes and said, "You needn't be looking like that," grinning in a mischievous way.

When they left they linked arms and huddled closer, an evening chill encouraging intimacy.

He loved the old pub she brought him to. They had started in an empty snug, till close. He thought the colours of her crocheted poncho were like echoes of the stained-glass windows. An old lady, thin and worn-looking but bright and chirpy in herself, joined them.

"Ah, you don't mind me joining you, do you dearie? It doesn't do for a lady to be seen in a pub on her own."

"Not at all, come on in," she said. He smiled agreement.

"Ah you're very kind. It's a shame to be interrupting young love."

They laughed together and reassured her once more. He was quietly pleased.

The old lady spoke to him, "Would you mind going to the bar for me, young man? I'll give you the money."

She reached into her bag, fumbling for a purse.

"It doesn't do for a lady to order drink at the bar, here you are."

He negotiated his way to the counter, the space outside the snug rapidly filling up with customers, a mixture of people of all ages and styles.

He was fascinated by the hissing of the gaslights; he had never seen working gaslights before. The gaslights, old tiled walls, and tobacco-coloured ceiling fashioned a mellowness entirely in harmony with his own feelings. He noted the signs on the walls stating that team colours were not allowed in the bar.

His accent, the rising levels of laughter, and easy flowing conversation made for some difficulties with the barman. Unfamiliar with the drinks and the coins, he fumbled at first, but then she was there again at his side to help him. She joked with the barman as they collected their drinks and change.

Gradually they were joined by more of her friends. They were easygoing, no-one concerned by a stranger popping up suddenly in their midst. They told jokes, interrupted each other, shared cigarettes. They talked about music they liked, books they'd read, films they'd seen. No-one spoke about religion, politics or sport.

When the talk came around to a new art exhibition, she became animated. She was passionate in her opinions, strongly defending her point of view. He remembered once playing for her a song about her being an artist, having everything she needed, being able to paint the daytime black.

As they left, heavily armoured police vehicles were gathered around the entrance to the hotel across the street. Their blue lights bounced off the old tiles adorning the pub's facade.

Traffic was being diverted away from the area.

"Come on," she hurried him along, both immediately anxious to be elsewhere, not wanting the day to end there.

In the quiet of the night she could feel his silent tears. Reaching across the narrow space from her bed, she felt for, found and held his hand. "It's OK," she whispered.

With his free hand he squeezed his eyes to dry them. He told her he knew that. He was even able to softly, laugh. It was healing laughter, free from self-pity.

When she had insisted on undressing in the dark he had known it would be like this. He had known it when he felt a long cotton nightdress brush against him as she turned down the quilt on the smaller bed. He told her he wasn't crying because of that. She was right. It was OK. But why, he wondered aloud, was it that women he felt so close to wanted him so much as a friend?

"I can sit with you quietly for ten minutes and it feels like I've told you everything and most of all, that you've heard me. That's why."

She got out of her bed and came over to him. They held each other tightly, quietly, in the dark. She kissed him once and said, "You are a really good friend." She emphasised the word *are*. "I don't want to lose that."

She went back to bed, saying, "We have a long day tomorrow, and we'd better sleep now."

Holding hands across the space between them, they fell asleep. They slept easily, both of them. Dreams kept them company and, in the morning, when he opened his eyes, he was looking at her looking at him.

Blue skies, a light wind, it was a morning full of promise. Taking the sunny side of the road, they strolled along together. He was content that the day should unfold whatever way it would. After the art gallery they bought ice-cream cones and sat on a bench outside the Victorian glasshouses, basking in sheltered warmth.

"We'll go outside town now, if that's all right with you?" Her eyes on his were open and honest, trusting. That was fine by him, he told her. He felt peaceful and calm; he smiled and told her this too.

"Then maybe a long walk in the country is just the thing." She patted his arm, looked at him and said, "Do us both the world of good."

They went to the open-air folk museum where they walked and talked for miles. Weaving their way from one relocated traditional home to another, they drew their own stories around them.

In silence when they absorbed one new place after another, they walked from the Antrim Weaver's Cottage to the Shepherd's House from the Mountains of Mourne.

At the little café he thanked her, holding one hand in both of his.

"You're a good friend," she hesitated, smiled and continued, "and at least you believe I'm an artist."

In the morning she brought him to the station. The unfinished drawings he had admired the night before were in the heavy portfolio satchel that dragged from her shoulder. He knew she needed to hurry, that she had to go, that she had taken the trouble to see him off safe, to say goodbye.

They hugged, he boarded, she was gone.

At Portadown the soldiers ignored him. Leaving, he was someone else's problem.

THE DOGS
Emma Hutton

Rós Blake was fifteen when the fulmars circled to scrape her flesh from the rocks of the island. The island that's surrounded by a cold, dark sea. Legend says it was made by the mother of a giant crossing the water to bring food back to her greedy son. As she walked, she cast soil from her apron into the water, creating stepping stones so she could easily pass. But she slipped and fell, and the soil tumbled out and over her, trapping her body beneath what is now this island. It is five miles long and two miles wide, and at its edges lurks the wreckage of ships. It is a place that is forever ripe with ending.

Rós' family put what was left of her body into an unlined casket and pushed it into the earth. A stone marked her final resting place and scratched across it was not her name, because we all knew where she was and where she'd been. The words on that stone were a plea, 'Forgive her, Father.' They said she'd fallen, been chased by the wild dogs up by the cliffs where we were told never to go. But nobody could fall from up where the dogs were because nobody ended up there by accident. We used to watch the dogs from afar, grey specks darting up across the earth to pull birds out of the sky. Everyone had a story to tell about the dogs, how they appeared in packs across the road to the church or the pub. Their orange eyes glowing and their jaws wide open. How they'd pulled a baby out through an open window. Even after they dug up the old well and found a baby's bones we still knew to say it was the dogs that had done it. It was easier that way.

It wasn't the first time Rós had fallen. A month before her body was broken across those rocks she'd been found down by the castle ruins. She'd been on her way to Judith McCabe's sixteenth birthday party but she'd never made it and Judith had never gotten the silver hair clip that Rós had carefully laid in a velvet-lined box taken from her mother's nightstand. Judith was one of Rós' girls—the girls we all wanted to be. There was Rós, Judith, Aoife Hannigan, Eimear McCrae and Catherine Corrigan. They moved through the island as if pitched and hit, swinging around corners like a pack of sirens, all dyed red hair and soft songs they learned from the radio. But it was Rós who everyone wanted to be, or be near. No matter what she did, no matter the names she called us or the lies she told about us, we wanted to be one of Rós' girls. To sit beside her, to have her pull our hair and whisper in our ear.

It was her brother who found her that night in a diaphanous pink dress that had belonged to their mother. He said it looked as though somebody had pushed her backwards into the claggy earth and she lay where she fell with her red hair circling her head like a newly minted saint. We imagined the soft pink material wound up around her hips but it wasn't. It was held in place with a twisted gold leather belt. The ruffled hem moved like waves in the wind, kissing the soles of her shoes. The shoes we all wanted. As she lay there, her arms sank into the earth and she gave out hot, sweet gasps because she wasn't dead. Not yet. She was only sleeping.

Every morning we went to her house and leaned against its white walls until we were ushered upstairs by her mother. Her quiet mother who looked too young to have a girl like Rós. In her bed, Rós looked rubbed out and drawn in again, blurred around the edges. She smelled like sugar in a pan caught just in time and she stuck in our throats and we felt her on our skin long after we left her. On the bedside table was a saucer full of rings that would turn fingers an underwater-green and a bottle of perfume, the liquid turned orange by the sun. Communion-white net curtains hung in the window and a cross over the bed. On the back of the door, her mother's pink dress. We crammed all this into the parts of us where it might fit, so that we could know her. We stayed until Rós' mother made us leave and then we watched her from the windows as she pulled Rós out of that bed, shaking her half-awake so she could guide her stumbling child to the bathroom where she propped her up on the toilet and told her to go. In the afternoons, when the priest came, he would hold Rós' head, whispering prayers to keep her awake while her mother filled her mouth with soft, wet food. Together they counted her chews.

Our mothers told us to hush when we asked questions and told us to pray for her. We tried to tell them about Rós' growing belly under all those bed covers but they pushed us away. We dug through our memories to find out how she came to be laid up in that bed with that belly. We remembered the story of her under the library stairs with the history teacher from the mainland. The story of the boys and her behind the community hall the night of the summer party. There were so many stories. We prayed for Rós on our knees and in boxes. We recited her name as we walked to school and back again, an incantation. Rós. Rós. Rós. At night, we breathed on our bedroom windows and plotted her name across the glass. We prayed she would wake up changed and come to us with hot hands. She would be sorry for the bad things she'd said about us. Sorry she had not seen us there in the background. She would paint her lips and then ours. Her jaw would crack from the weight of the apologies that could not wait to escape from her mouth. She would put our hands on her belly and whisper in our ears. Eventually she did wake, but not for us and not for long. The words we wanted to hear were caught against the rocks like her bones when she threw her body from the cliffs up by where the dogs were.

After she was gone, we watched the girls, Rós' girls, more closely. Watched as they huddled in corners pushing hair out of each other's faces. They were quiet and we only ever heard them when they sang along to the childish songs they had begun to sing. Sometimes we thought we saw them out at night, through kitchen windows as we scraped the dinner plates. They walked down to the beach and up through the fields, close to where the dogs were until we couldn't see them anymore. It wasn't long until they fell. Judith was first. She'd been out swimming when mid-breaststroke she fell asleep. A boy took off his shoes and swam out to drag her back onto the shore. He leant over her body about to give her mouth-to-mouth when she started to softly snore. The black of her wet swimming costume clung to her rounded belly and anyone who looked could see there was a baby there. Aoife was found a few days later on the back seat of the old school bus, a burnt-out cigarette between her fingers, headphones still on, blue biro on the back of her hand spelling out 'Rós'. Eimear fell in the chemist and half a dozen brand new red lipsticks rolled out of her knickers and across the shop floor. Catherine climbed into bed one night and simply did not wake up to her mother's calls in the morning. And that's where she stayed for the next month.

At first they said it was a trick, then they said it was a disease. A disease passed from Rós. We hoped it was contagious. We wanted to be like them, even now. We tried to call in at their houses, skipping ahead of the boys that lined the walls outside but the mothers wouldn't let us inside. 'Go away, girls. And take those boys with you.' We performed rituals that we hoped would bring them back into the waking world, burying things we'd found in their lockers at school—Judith's pink silky headscarf, Eimear's orange-scented nail polish, Aoife's mixtapes. We lit candles and sang their favourite songs. As the girls lay in their beds we found wild flower posies wedged between the gaps of the stone walls of our houses. Squares of chocolate were pressed into our palms as we passed boys in the school corridor. The boys saw us and we let them come to us to drown out the din of the sea. It was our turn and as we walked from our houses into the night no-one stopped us. We ran our fingers across the boys' edges and let them weigh us into the earth. Our necks grew wet as we lost count of the stars. We zigzagged home across the fields pulling sheeps' wool out of the barbed wire fences to soak up the blood between our thighs. In our beds we listened to the dogs make noises in the darkness.

They say whatever comes within reach of the shores belongs to the island and when the bodies of Judith, Aoife, Eimear, Catherine and a handful of wild dogs washed up onto the beach it was clear the island had claimed them. They'd been seen, just before dawn, walking hand in hand up across the fields in their nightdresses to where the dogs were. The story goes that they danced, turning in circles with their arms lifted to the sky and when the dogs started to leap from the cliffs, they followed.

A woman had seen them out there before they jumped. 'They hurled themselves out into that sky like there was nothing to fear. As if they would fly.'

Their wave-beaten bodies were plucked from the shore and dropped into the earth a day later. Not a word was said about all the lives being buried.

As we watched the mothers stand over their dead daughters, wringing their soft hands, we realised that they too were girls of the island.

In the days that passed, men went up to the place where the dogs were, carrying guns they used to cull birds in spring. The morning they returned, smoke drifted down off the cliffs and across the fields. It stuck in our hair for days. The smell of death. Of dogs.

We had started to dream of the girls. We saw them under water, weaving through the lost ships as they called out to us, tugging at the laces of our shoes, tangling us to them. We listened to their sweet songs and let the stones the boys threw crack against our windows. We lay there, letting the clawing inside our bellies grow until the brightest moon called us out of our beds and into the black, glassy water. We waded out until we lost our footing and reached out for hands we could not see. Soft hands that dragged our heavy bodies onto boats and pushed out into the sea, away from the black rock that had buried so many of us.

We were the girls of the island. We were the girls who ran with the dogs. The girls who flew.

Years of Sleep
Emily O'Grady

Jenny's feet are swollen as berries when the Falcon pulls into the bus station. Sweat suctions her blouse to her back and she stands and reaches for her suitcase. Vinnie told her he'd pick her up at three, but she called his mobile when she got off the bus and it rang out to voicemail. It's past four now, and Jenny steps towards the car. It's not until the man behind the wheel rolls down the tinted window that she realises her mistake.

'Vinnie's stuck at work,' the stranger calls out. 'He'll pick you up from mine when he knocks off.'

Jenny squints at the man. He looks to be in his late thirties, a few years older than her. An elaborate tattoo stains his bicep and disappears into his shirtsleeve. Jenny takes a step back, grips her suitcase handle tight. 'I can wait here for him,' she says. 'No trouble.'

'Can't leave you here to cook,' he says, reaching across to open the passenger door. 'In you get.'

Jenny looks down the street. A skinny teenager comes out of the bakery next to the station, pulls a cream bun out of a paper bag. She can see the glisten of red jam, the same colour as the stone on her ring finger. She turns back to the man, lifts her hand to shade the sun from her eyes. 'How d'you know Vinnie, then?'

'We're mates. He asked me to pick you up.'

She would have insisted on waiting for Vinnie if it weren't so hot. But she can't bear another second of it: the stretch of brick, the drone of flies, the fiery scorch of grass.

Jenny lugs her suitcase and garment bag to the car, heaves them into the backseat and climbs into the front. The man has pushed his sunglasses onto his head. His eyes are blue and pale.

'Rob,' he says. 'Good to meet you.' He wraps his arm around the back of her headrest, looks through the rear windscreen and reverses to face back the way he'd come. 'Big suitcase for a weekend.'

'I'm going overseas after James and Kayla's wedding.' Jenny says. 'I leave on Monday.'

'Where're you going?'

'California.'

'What for?'

'Just a holiday.'

He glances over at Jenny, pulls the sun visor down. 'I had a mate who went to the States a couple years back, started chatting to this girl on the street, perfectly nice girl he said, but after a minute a copper pulls up, charges him for solicitation, if you can believe it.' Rob fiddles with the radio, surfs through stations. 'I'm ten minutes out of town, just past the industrial estate. Do you know it?'

'I've only been here once,' Jenny says, 'when I was a kid.'

'Never came to visit Vinnie? He's been here what, five, six years now?'

Jenny shakes her head.

'Thought you were good mates,' Rob says. 'That's what Vinnie says.'

'I have to look after my mother,' Jenny says, stretching her hands over her thighs. She wonders if Rob has noticed the ring. It's the first time she's worn it in public though she bought it at Cash Converters back in August. When she sent Lou a picture he said it was perfect, exactly what he would've chosen for her, and that he'll arrange for his aunt to pay her back when Jenny gets to Fresno. It makes her finger itch, and she picks at the skin flaking around the gold band. The cream-bun stone shines in the light.

Rob turns up the volume and something electronic blasts from the speakers. Jenny turns to the window; Federation homes flicker by, immaculate lawns with garden beds sprouting hydrangeas and gerberas. As they move further from town; squat timber bungalows, the occasional paddock with scrawny horses pining at the fence. It's not until they cross over a pathetic river that Jenny becomes aware of the distance travelled. They've been driving longer that ten minutes, and she feels dizzy with carsickness, is hit with a feeling of dread that the road is endless. That they are barreling into nothing.

The fresh remains of a roo flashes by, its rusty fur vibrant. Another two smeared on the asphalt a trucks-length up the road. 'You can just drop me at Vinnie's place.' She tries to sound casual but her voice is thin. 'Or back to town. I can wait there till he's done.'

Rob flicks on his left indicator, though there are no other cars in sight. 'You'll be mauled to death at this hour,' he says. The sun glares on the horizon. Glitters of heat make blur in the distance. 'They like girls, especially.'

'Pardon?'

'The midges,' he says. 'They're shocking this time of year.'

Rob pulls up in front of a small brick house. Jenny can see a cluster of similar houses further up the street, a shopping trolley corpsed in the scrub. She gathers her things and follows him to the front door. It's unlocked, and Rob whacks open the flyscreen. Jenny slips off her shoes, leaves her suitcase and dress by the front door.

As they enter the kitchen the phone begins to ring.

'Make yourself at home,' Rob says, and disappears into the hall. The ceiling fan clicks angrily above Jenny's head. She moves to the edge of the room to escape its flight path, tries to listen to the phone conversation, but Rob's voice is muffled through the walls.

She waits for Rob to appear, but the minutes drag. Jenny scans the kitchen. It's spotless, the morning's breakfast dishes drying in the rack. An oven mitt speckled with shamrocks hangs from a hook above the oven. On the fridge, alphabet magnets spell out Rob's name.

Jenny can feel him before she sees him.

'That was Vinnie,' Rob announces from doorway. 'He'll be a couple hours still. Some girl's been found tied up in a caravan out near the dam. Bleach in her throat. Half dead, he reckons. Says he needs to get the story written up for tomorrow.'

Jenny tries to feel sorry for the girl. 'I might call him back then. Can I use your phone?'

'Reception is pretty fuzzy out here. Could hardly hear him.'

Jenny moves past Rob, towards the front door where she left her things. She'll charge her phone, send Vinnie a text. Tell him to sort himself and hurry up. But her suitcase is gone; her shoes and dress as well.

Rob clears his throat. 'I've put your stuff in there.' He points towards a closed door down the hall.

Jenny follows him, and he moves aside to let Jenny enter first. The walls are painted lavender, and alien-coloured glow stickers speckle the ceiling, netball trophies along the windowsill. The bedspread is printed with a Disney princess. The carpet is soft beneath her feet.

'This is May's room,' Rob says. 'She's only here a couple times a month. Lives with her mum closer to town.' He picks up a photo from the chest of drawers: a little girl sitting at the bottom of a slippery dip. Gummy smile, wispy hair.

'Looks a bit like you,' Jenny says, though Rob and the child look nothing alike. 'The eyes, and the nose.'

'You reckon?' He sounds pleased. 'Everyone says she looks like Rhi.' Rob sets the photo down, nods toward the garment bag hanging from the wardrobe handle. 'That your dress then?' he says. 'For the wedding? School friends, right? Vinnie said it'll be a bit of a reunion.'

Before she can answer, Rob strides over and zips the bag open. The dress is pale purple, similar to the colour licking the walls. It has a stiff collar, and embroidered daisies scattered on the mesh covering the décolletage. The dress belongs to her mother. She's packed safety pins in her toiletries bag to hem the armholes, stop them from billowing.

'Your husband not invited, then?'

Jenny's ring feels like a weight. 'Fiancé,' she says. The word tastes girlish in her mouth. Sticky.

Rob stares at the dress. 'Good colour, that,' he says. 'It'll suit you. It'll bring out your eyes.'

✻

Back in the kitchen, Rob takes a parcel out of the fridge. 'D'you like barra?'

'Don't go to any trouble,' Jenny says. She wonders how much longer Vinnie will be. They're supposed to go to the pub for dinner, her shout. She'd taken out two crisp twenties from the ATM before boarding the bus.

'It's what I was having anyway.' Rob places the fish on the bench. He hands her a couple of potatoes, a paring knife. 'Scraps go in that,' he says, nodding towards an ice-cream container by the sink. She feels like a child, being given her jobs. But she peels the potatoes, makes sure to do a good job of it.

Jenny rinses the red dirt from her hands, asks for the bathroom. She closes the door and quickly undresses. She takes off her wig and rests it on the hook behind the door. Her bun has come loose, and she shakes out her hair, can feel sweat on her fingertips. She pulls off a stream of toilet paper and dampens it under the sink, runs the wad over her neck, under her arms, between her breasts. She dumps the wad into the toilet and sits down. She can hear Rob's footsteps outside the door.

When she's done she washes her hands, sticks her head under the faucet. The water doesn't taste right. She looks at her watch. It's almost six. Back home, her mother will be settling down to watch the news over Cruskits and cheese.

Jenny pulls back the shower curtain. The products in the caddy are all silver and navy, except for the peach loofah hanging over the tap. There's a spatter of dark hairs in the tub, like cracks in the ceramic. She imagines Rob in the shower, the metallic water giving the steam a bloody tang. She touches the loofah and it's dry and crisp.

✻

They sit at the kitchen table. Rob has set out a jar of mayo and half a lemon. The fillets are full of bones, and they pick them out of their mouths, set them at the rims of their plates. The fluorescents are brassy and the moths shadows flicker in the beam of light above their heads. After they eat, Rob scrapes their bones into the bin and starts washing up. Jenny stands around, sends Vinnie another text. She grabs a tea towel but Rob takes it from her and places it on top of the microwave.

'More hygienic to let them drip dry,' he says.

Rob lights a mosquito coil, gets a round of beers from the fridge. They sit on the patio. The last of the sun glows a chemical orange, and the feeding birds are black against the sky, their squawks heinous.

Rob presses a bottle top against his palm. She asks him what he does for work.

'Nothing,' Rob says.

'Right,' Jenny says. 'Thought you must've been a tradie.'

'Why'd you think that?'

'I don't know. I just thought...'

Rob takes a sip of beer. 'I used to be a disability support worker, but after I won the lotto, I thought, what's the point? I don't need the money, not for a little while anyway.'

'You won the lotto?'

'1.3 mil.'

'You're joking?'

'Dead set.'

'What'd you spend it on?'

'Paid off the house, bought a new car. Had tenderloin for tea every night for a couple weeks but got sick of that pretty quick. I'm veggo now, can you believe? Except for fish, that is.' Jenny can't tell if he is dead set, but his face is straight and he keeps on. 'That's how I know Vinnie. He did a story on me, right after I won. Front page of the local rag.'

The beer has turned Jenny's body heavy. She can see clearly the life she's leaving behind, dull and coarse as the prickles that spread across Rob's lawn, while the future radiates in a ball of light above her head.

Jenny tells Rob she'll be right back and slips into the child's bedroom, wheels her suitcase out to the patio. She kneels down and unzips it. She watches Rob's glance over the heads of hair, three of them, like thick, shiny pelts. Sitting at the top of the suitcase they look disturbing, like she is carting around severed heads. She takes one out, strawberry blonde and thick as horsehair, holds it over her fist like a hand puppet.

Rob's eye's narrow. 'You're not sick, are you?'

'No,' she says. She takes off the wig she's wearing, a dark bob, and tips her head upside down, fits the blonde wig on. Rob reaches over and touches a strand of the hair as though checking it's real, then jerks his hand back, startled to find out it is.

✳

Jenny told her mother she booked a tour along the West Coast: San Diego, Death Valley, Monterey. When she showed her the passport that had just arrived in the post, her mother stared at the ID page. 'When'd you sneak off and get this done?' she said.

Jenny handed her the brochures she'd gotten from the travel agent, and she hadn't asked questions after that. Jenny arranged for Lou's aunt to pick her up from the airport. She'll stay the night on her couch in Fresno and then get a bus south, find a motel in Corcoran. The prison isn't far from the town centre, and in his last letter Lou told Jenny her name was on the visitors' list. Jenny is in contact with Lou's aunt, and a cousin Lou says was closer to him than his own brother, who lives in the Midwest with his wife and five kids and hasn't contacted Lou since the trial, not even a phone call. Yolanda and Joseph offered to pass her emails along to Lou, but Jenny prefers letters.

Back when it began, Jenny asked her mother to take her picture against the tin shed in the soft morning light, told her it was for the work newsletter at the Real Estate. She chose the blonde wig and her mother uncapped a bullet of lipstick, smudged it onto Jenny's lips and cheeks. Jenny's mother had to sit down to take the photo. The walk from the house to the shed left her short of breath, but she hitched her dress up over her knees and didn't complain even when a spidery rash flushed from her chest up her neck.

She sent Lou the photo, and in his reply he told her she looked like Jayne Mansfield—that hair!—and that his life was like an endless year of sleep, but the photo of her against the sparkling silver was waking him up. She'd slipped the letter back into its envelope, added it to the folder. Her secret life, her inexplicable future.

*

They have another beer. Vinnie and the coming weekend are far from her mind. The air has lost its wetness by the time Rob slips into the house. Jenny thinks he's getting more drinks, but he comes back holding the lavender dress. It hovers in his hands like a phantom. He presses it toward Jenny, far from his body, like he's passing a baby back to its mother.

'Put it on,' Rob says. His grin is dopey, and for a moment something deeply sweet flashes across his face.

Jenny takes the dress. She feels silly but heads into the purple bedroom to undress. She contorts her arms behind her back to zip up, folds her shorts and blouse and leaves them at the end of the bed.

Back on the patio, Rob is leaning against the railing. He sets down his beer, wipes his mouth with the back of his hand. 'Turn around,' he says, quietly.

'What?'

'A twirl,' he says. 'Do a twirl.'

The night is black now. She looks in the direction of Rob's neighbours, but no lights are on. She hasn't heard a car drive past all evening, and doesn't realise she had that piece of information inside her, does not remember noticing or not noticing the cars. But she must remember, because her brain is telling her so.

Jenny does as she is told. As she turns, an image drifts across her mind: a child playing netball down at the courts. She's not sure who it is. It doesn't matter. It could be anyone. She concentrates hard on the image: pudgy-girl legs under a pleated skirt, crop-top tight against a chest. Scabbed knees. She thinks that if she focuses hard enough on this tiny, bright moment then she can leave her body. That her body will become a shell, and whatever else she is made of will separate and hover over the patio and the estate, until she is at the courts, the sound of the umpire whistles ringing like church bells.

Rob's hand pulls her back. He is standing now, and she can smell fish and beer on his breath. He rubs his thumb against the inside of her wrist, his fingers blistering against that soft part of her, and stares not at her eyes, but at her hair. With his other hand he reaches for her.

An invisible animal makes a mouth-sound from deep in the grass. Jenny feels the ball of light begin to fade from above her head. She wonders what time it is in California. The cusp of dawn, she decides. The sun warm over the desert. The smell of the orange orchards light and clean.

A Little Salt
Yvonne Singh

The night air is thick and still, like caramel cooling in the pan—all the day's work and hopes and dreams setting slowly. Aunty Longgal takes a deep breath and places Frankie's battered old shoes on the front porch. The soles have given way, and the heels done mashed down. Longgal smiles—it's almost as if dem old brogues grinning at she.

She closes the door, walks back inside and is about to settle down in she chair but hesitates, her body swaying like a stick of cane. She makes her way to the kitchen to get the salt-shaker that sits next to the toaster. *Damn thing cover in crumbs.* She brushes it carefully with she flannel dress, twists the lid to pour, opens the door and leaves a mound of salt next to the shoe. *Well you can't be too careful now, can you?*

She folds into the old Chesterfield, her bony fingers reaching for the wireless knob. Should be a nice play on at this time of night. Nice talk-talk show. People with plummy voices and likkle problem, making fuss-fuss. At least then she forget. Man, people get desperate now. But the radio just hiss at her. She sighs and reaches for the rum and sticky shot glass on the sill and pours herself an amber slug, willing on the peace that sleep brings.

But that alsatian starts one hell of a bark next door, startling Longgal from she chair. Neighbour have him tie up outside all night. Damn thing never quiet. Longgal sucks she teeth and brushes she dress, the white lily pattern all sandy with breadcrumbs, and tries to settle.

It's when she fall asleep again that the boys' eyes come for she—all wet and glassy with tears, and she recalls in her dreams what happen that day.

*

'Come quick, Aunty Longgal, Mummy need doctor.'

Longgal in no hurry. She'd just been in town all morning and was weighed down with packet. In fact all Longgal want is a cup of sweet tea and a slice of black cake, except this likkle man pulling at she sleeve, nearly knocking Longgal over on she own porch.

'Come, mummy sick.' The boy's bandy legs stick out from he raggedy shorts and the dusty skin of his elbows play patchwork against the frayed thread of his sleeve.

Longgal recognise him—one of the seamstress's children from the shanty huts at the top of the lane, the eldest maybe, he look about eight. She'd hear de gossip: the woman husband left she earlier this year and now she has to mind all four children alone.

'Me feet weary. Me wan for sit down,' she say. 'What wrong with yuh mummy that you have fire so?'

'Man tek mummy jewellery and nah give she money. She drink something bad. She so sad. Please help her, aunty.'

Longgal shake she head, her heart sinking. She usher the boy into her house, placing she bags on the floor. He stand by the door, he head way too big for his tiny body, twitching like a marabunta.

Longgal eye him as he take in the red earth floor, the lace throw on she armchair, the picture of Frankie on the oak sideboard all smart and handsome in he brass button policeman uniform—Guyana's finest. The boy's eyes grow big when he see the stuffed baby crocodile between she china plate, its jaws wrenched wide. Longgal glad she tuck away de bleached fish bones in she cabinet—too many picanniny come in and fiddle with dem and dem not toy.

'Your ma need medicine not dat kind of thing,' say Longgal.

Longgal leave the door ajar as she goes into the kitchen. 'Y'all wait here. I need to get some ting to make Mummy better.'

Longgal reach for she medicine bag at the top of the fridge—de thing heavy like a sack of breadfruit. She inch it slowly into she arms, careful not to harm de inside. She tek time to check all of it contents, muttering under she breath. All the while the boy watching she—him like one of dem wind-up doll, he itching to go.

'Come we leave now,' she say, snapping the clasp shut.

The boy push open the door and skitter across the porch. Once he start moving, he nah cease up, he drag Longgal on a merry dance across the wrinkled earth, his jelly sandals flapping up little dust clouds.

Longgal stride behind him, the medicine bag bumping gently against she thigh. No one say anything as she pass the candy-coloured houses on the main street, they just watch she: the teenage girls gossiping in dey short shorts stand rigid like Longgal have snakes for hair. Only old man Rajin nod he head—him always on he porch reclining in he Berbice chair his white ash heels reflecting the midday sun.

The boy's shack is at the end of the row—in the distance, Longgal can see the cane fields seamed by the silver line of the Essequibo. The day so hot, de image quivers like a mirage. Three likkle children drowning in Arsenal shirts stand on a stretch of parched grass outside de broke down place—all of dem have the same haunted look as dey brother: eyes dark and wide, hollowed cheeks, mouths pursed into tiny beaks. Longgal see the corrugated iron roof tip sideways and the dents in the shack's bleached wooden slats, and her heart bleed a little fuh all of dem.

'All you stay here,' she say. She tall shadow loom over them like a hawk about to snare some baby owls. The children huddle together and nod. Longgal wish people weren't so scare of she.

Longgal push the door hinge with she knuckle, the paint bobble on it like a case of pox. It creak open. The older boy behind she cradling she skirt. On the stone floor is a scratch of a woman dressed in a turquoise sari, her body bent double in pain. White froth bubbles at the corner of her lips and her forehead gleams with sweat. Her thin hair is twisted into a tight bun, but a strand has come loose framing she sweet, heart-shaped face. Longgal looks into the woman's eyes—she sees fear, sadness and pain.

'Oi sista, why you gwan do this for? You nah think of your picanniny,' Longgal exclaim.

The woman rasps fuh breath.

Longgal hasten to the sink at the back of the room. She see a grey double mattress in de corner veiled by a mosquito net which she guess fits all of dem. She wets a cloth and crouches down, pressing it against the woman head.

The boy stand there, twitching.

'Mummy gonna be alright?' he ask.

Longgal don't know wha' for say. She take the cloth and sap the woman's lips.

'You know wha' Mummy tek?'

The boy patter towards the cupboard under the sink and hold up a white plastic bottle. GRAMOXONE is spelt out in big blue type on the label. 'I think this.'

Aunty Longgal shoulders slump—she feels as powerless as a rag doll. All she can think of is the children standing outside—what kind of life for them now?

Nothing in her bag will work, the milk of magnesia, the charcoal pills. The woman too far gone, she shivering, de poison muddying her blood. She can try and make she sick for the boy's sake.

'Fetch me a glass of water,' she say to the boy.

The boy go to the sink and bring back a red plastic beaker. Longgal heave the woman into she lap, using her right arm to pin she in a firm embrace. She tek the cup from the boy, while her left hand seek out the solid floor.

She try to hold de woman but she start to toss and turn, she slippery like eel, and Longgal can't make she still fuh drink.

'Hold she feet,' she say to the boy but he not strong enough and the woman in real pain now, arching she back and clenching she teeth. She let out one yell and de boy scare and let go. The woman tumble right back into Longgal, knocking she chin and making her teeth slice her tongue. Longgal wan' for scream too, but the boy trust her, he need her for help.

'Get Rajin,' she say to the boy. 'Tell him to call hospital and give him all yuh address.'

The boy stand there, twitching again.

She grip the woman again to get she still fuh drink. Their limbs blur, the nylon sari scratch she skin like pumice and the stench of ammonia on the woman breath make she want to retch. The water spill—a dark stain on the concrete. Longgal curse.

'But what about Mummy?' say the boy. 'Can't you help her?'

Longgal stare into those deep dark pools. 'I sorry child there is nothing I can do for she.'

'Plenty people tek dey life now,' say old man Rajin to she as the ambulance pull away, the moles on his right cheek making pattern like constellation. 'And we a small country.'

'You can blame de fact we poor, you can blame de fact we drink, you can blame de British for dragging we here to cut sugar, but I blame dat preacher for coming here and doing him nonsense, it he alone curse this land.'

*

'Nathan, Nathan, Wake up Nathan.'

If it's not the dog, or the cock crowing, it's that woman next door but one, yelling like a fishwife on the port of Demerara. Longgal wakes with a start. She still in she flannel dress. She smooths she hair, which feels rough like Brillo pad, and goes outside to collect Frankie's shoes. She stops when she sees that the large salt mound has been broken into five small hillocks. She curse under she breath.

Longgal picks up de shoe and she remembers how she Frankie's spade-like hands used to shine dat shoe with Cherry Blossom until he could see his face. Man, he was so proud of that job. That is... until that day.

That day he never speak. And the next day he never speak. And three weeks after he never speak. Longgal was young then and pretty and slim—she wore her hair twist in ringlets and she knew on a good day she could rival Shakira Baksh, that Miss Guyana who marry dat movie star Michael Caine. She and Frankie had been married for four years—he was the only boy in the class taller than she. And he used to tell she everything. Every case, every story, he ask Longgal opinion. Longgal only a typist but she love dem crime story, why people act so—for money, for love, always some reason.

But this preacher, no one know why he act, it like he possessed by the devil. Frankie no say a word about it. She read the paper—how they shot up the Congressman, she read how he poison he flock, she see the pictures—the rows of aluminium caskets at the airport trussed up in thick elastic. Man, big story. All those people dead. All world eyes on Guyana. And we a small country. US troops stomping Georgetown street. But Frankie no say a word.

She careful not to push but one day he come home drunk and acting de fool, and she ask him cos she fed up because they use to fit together like puzzle and now it like chicken wire weave between dem. But she wish she hadn't ask because what he say still make her cry even now.

Frankie collapse into the dining chair and hold he huge head in his hands. 'I haven't tell you Longgal because if I tell you, it's like I make it real. At the moment it still a nightmare.'

She look into his soft brown eyes and they red-rimmed with suffering. 'Tell me what happened in the interior,' she say.

'We were called to the jungle the next morning after the Congressman and the five of dem kill.' He pause and look at the floor. 'We arm with guns cos we think dem People Temple nutter going to start a fight and we can't hardly see we rifle muzzle because the rain come down so hard, steam coming up from the jungle floor and everything shrouded in thick white mist, like cotton wool, man.'

'We treading so-so quiet, almost tip-toe. And then one of us fall and then another and then another, and we think that they leave a trap for we, tripping us with logs or some such thing. Then one boy start screaming so loud like he lung going to burst.' Frankie shutter his eyes.

'And we turn round to shut him up. But he pointing to the floor, he mouth wide open and scare, drooling like a madman. And we look down to see what he see. And we see through the mist and they no logs, they bodies, more bodies than we can count. And we all screaming now. Cos the jungle come for these bodies, the animals, the bugs, and they bloat up and swell, and dat stench is awful. And we think that maybe 300 or 400 people die at first. But he stack them in layers: adults on top, ol' people underneath and likkle children at de bottom. He kill nearly a thousand. He wipe out all of dem...'

Frankie whole body shudder and he weep like she never see him weep before. Longgal hold him but she know he broken.

That was forty years ago and Frankie gone twenty. Old man Rajin right, Longgal know what she got fuh do.

✳

It's here it happened—if she close she eyes she can hear the echoes of screams. This earth laden with sorrow, like it bruise deep. Shadows flit beside she—insects, birds, who knows? Everything old here and know what went on. Heavy trunks guard she, their thick creepers hissing and stretching like they wan' for hear. The moon just a fingernail of light, the sky dark and stern, and bear down upon she like saucepan lid.

She reach into she bag and she take out a couple of blistered jars filled with powders and the salt—always salt because Gramma said it slows dem jumbees down. She twist the jars open and slowly begin to pour.

ARGUMENT OF SITUATIONS
Shangyang Fang

I was thinking, while making love, *this is beautiful*—this

fine craftsmanship of his skin, the texture of wintry river.

I pinched him, three inches above his coccyx, so that he knew

I was still here, still in an argument with Fan Kuan's

inkwash painting, where an old man, a white-gowned literatus,

dissolves into the landscape as a plastic bag into clouds.

The man walks in the mountains. *No, he walks on rivers.*

The man moves among shapes. *He travels through colors.*

The mountains are an addendum of his silvergrass sandals.

Wrong, his embroidered sleeves are streaklines of trees.

None could persuade the other, as my fingers counted

his cervical spine, seven vertebrae that held up

a minute heaven in my hand. But it isn't important.

It is not, I said. It is just a man made of brushstrokes

moving in a crowd of brushstrokes. The man walks

inside himself. The string quartet of the tap water

streamed into a vase. My arms coursed around his waist.

We didn't buy any flowers for the vase. *It's ok.*

The sunlight would soon fabricate a bouquet of gladiolas.

To walk on a mountain for so long, he must desire

nothing. *Nothing must be a difficult desire.* Like the smell

of lemon, of cut pear, its wounds of snow. The man

must be tired. *He might.* He might be lonely.

He must be. The coastline of his spine, the alpine

of his cheekbone—here was where we stopped—this

periphery of skin, this cold, palpable remoteness

I held. The dispute persisted. Are you tired? *I'm ok.*

That means you are tired. *You're bitter.*

Whatever you say. If my hands departed from his skin,

the heaven would collapse. The limit remained

even though we had used the same soap, same shampoo;

we scented like the singularity of one cherry bloom.

The vase stayed empty, the sky started to rain.

My toothbrush leaned against his.

The man must be lonely, I said. *No, the mountain*

is never lonely. Burying my forehead inside his shoulder

blades, the mountain is making itself a man.

László Kovács and His Sons Cross the Border
Ron Carey

The Russian border guards are slow to leave
Their bewildered prisoners. But for a song
They sell their watches, helmets, all the gear
That turns a man into a soldier and back into
A man. When, finally, they leave, they take
Everything not nailed down; ripping the light
From the walls, the wires, the ceramic toilets,
All the forensic evidence of their existence.
Days later, László takes his two blonde sons
Out of their grey school. Outside, he tries
To shake them free but the grey is inclined
To hold on. With some garish manipulation
Of his hands, he produces two white flowers
And locates them under the boys' jumpers,
Under their shirts, up against their hearts.
He places the boys in the small metal egg
Of his car and drives to the border post
With Austria, where he crosses and crosses
And crosses again, testing their future.

AT THE TORTURERS' CONVENTION
Chloe Wilson

Everyone's fingernails are clean.
The weak tea quivers
in its polystyrene. Someone twists

the wrapper from a complimentary mint,
someone dabs ketchup
from his lapel, having decimated

breakfast. The projector
hums, one speaker pops their consonants,
another mumbles, delegates doodle

with customary discretion,
applaud the innovations in method
and application, enjoy the bickering,

the intergenerational frustration:
blunt instrument versus megahertz.
At the official dinner, the steak

is served well done. Everyone knows
to let the knife do the work, and when
the covers band starts up, they dance,

awkwardly at first, then with increasing
joie de vivre. They thrust and grind.
The exertion makes them sweat. No need

to be careful now — everyone can get reckless,
break a glass, knowing all of that dark wine
will vanish into the dark carpet.

THE DISTANT SOUND OF BEES
Molly Bashaw

Nights I can still see my dead mother
walk across her garden towards the field
as though across water, sinking through
as she bends to take something with her,
a weed, a potato bug. I wake with honey
stuck in my hair and go every day now
to that field, driving my music stand into
the soil, adjusting it like an antenna. But
she is done with words and has advanced
into the world. I have been meaning to
design a little flag for that place, a brown
silk-screened flag with a hill, a horse, three
stars, a squirrel. In winter I write her letters
in the frost on my window, I melt the crystal ferns
with my thumbs in spelling-bee words for her:
chrysanthemum, ecophagy, euonym, hireath.

In the second-hand shop where she used to go
I stare into the window at an old-fashioned
sewing machine, imagine its needle singing,
imagine it sews the ground like a plow.
In summer I walk barefoot over the places
she once walked. And when the dogs on our street
lift their heads to howl or bark, I lift mine with them,
though it is just the rain coming down toward
our faces, the rain relenting again, opening
its doors to us as though we had knocked, as though
we were holding out our hands to it.

THE ROAD TO SCHOOL No. 10
Elena Croitoru

By then, our churches had been rebuilt
but God did not return.
The older communists retreated
into their flats and I would walk
under their balconies,
along fossilised pavements,
on my way to school no. 10.

Sometimes I would see a man,
naked from the waist up
or down, I can't remember.
He would macerate his arms
in liquor, then he would wave
and I would wonder
if my homework was good enough
to get me out.

Sometimes I would break
into the stadium which took
the loneliness out of our town,
and encircled it with wooden benches.
Its silence made me think
about the places we called home.

Sometimes I would run
into the girl who told me
not to laugh, before she showed me
her two missing knuckles.
I nodded because I knew
how that felt. Those bones were
the first things she noticed about me.

Sometimes I grew, not up but sideways,
building a new century city in my mind,
shedding the concrete skins of tower blocks,
putting up one glass panel after another,
so we could all see
what our country had done to our people.

EXTINCTION
Alan Elyshevitz

The girl competes for hair color while the boy
wears black among the robins. She's a composite
of honorable mentions and a quick blouse
snatched from a laundry line. His heartache stems
from the senseless Alpine height of athletes.
These little anarchies grind their teeth, their nights
like a memory of screed. In time they meet,
they mate, passing an invoice from hand to hand.
With skin mollified by topical cream, they lose
the smoke other animals sense. The first fish
to waddle upon the sand could almost smell
the iron forge and the hooks forthcoming.
The last descendant of girl and boy is sure to be
a ruthless angler who dies when the rivers run out.

GRAMMAR, GUNPOWDER

Timons Esaias

The plural of cannon
is cannon,
because the
first cannon is already
too many, and others
just more
of the same.

The plural of ammunition
is ammunition.

More than one pain
is more pain.
Death, more death.

PORTRAIT OF MOTHER WITH A DAGGER
Shangyang Fang

My Mother used to beat me

    nightly.

Tonight, she decides to kill

    herself.

I'm not supposed to help.

    Her blood

        seeping from the bathtub, she is

    beautiful.

        Her body a wineglass

    brimming

        with a metallic, rusty beverage, ready

    to serve.

Tonight, the friendless poplar

    resumes

its lifelong practice of one

    pantomime,

while the osmanthus blossoms

    fissure

        into a hundred makeshift laughters. With

    a dagger

        welding in her belly, Mother is rehearsing

    Cleopatra,

        or Phaedra

    murdered

with a bite of love and guilt.

    There she is,

netherside of the theatrical light,

    an iron tail

at her front, half-male, half-fe-

    male.

        No, she is giving birth to an iron

child.
But Mother, Ma, Mama,
the word,
two repetitive vowels of yearning;
two silent
consonants seal lips to form
a shape of kissing,
is phonetically identical to Horse
in Chinese.
How I wish you were a sweating
horse, Ma,
so I could take you out for a meaningful
walk,
lather your belly that once
sharpened
my body like a blade. The incision
I made
inside you fit perfectly to my
shape.
I'd brush your mane, brown
wavelets
of a lake, where I'd drown
my lips
to impress a lasting wound in you.
As you
force your lips against
a cold
faucet, your face in the sink.
The soft
cathedrals of your breasts
no longer
raw pears with volition to drop.
The dagger
powerless without your hand.

ANDROMACHE
Natalie Ann Holborow

Assume I am wearing black. Assume I have swathed myself
in the hollow shades of his bruised knees, dust-clogged and sticky,
assume I am leaching away with him. The tracks of his belly
      scars the dirt. Does anyone ask for his wife,

hair dripping over the Trojan walls, towering ten feet over
the beetled men below, gleaming up and blinking through her?
Assume the wind blew me over the edge of the wall, quiet
      and pale as salt. Hear me say nothing at all.

See these living hands. Hear the smack of my palms
against stone, blood coiling its way to my heart, bind me tough
as a horseman's rope. Blow my bones to polished pipes
      they play when great men fall. For me,

no tune at all if I should choose to stagger up,
sway on broken toes, burst my lungs screaming for
the dead man's bones with our only child tumbling
      over crumbling stone in a gasp of blood and milk.

When Hector cracked his back behind the chariot,
when the bruises flowered blue, when our only baby spiralled
like sycamore, the Gods, I felt it too – I called *Astayanax*,
      I called *Hector*. Who called *Andromache*? Who?

IN THE HOUR BETWEEN WORK & THE MUSEUM'S CLOSE
Gabe Kruis

Upon Visiting "Like Life: Sculpture, Color, & the Body (1300 — Now)"

Through the curtains that divide the rooms, the silhouettes
of statues & patrons blend and, indistinct, if only briefly,
it's as if both were made of marble, as I, on the other side,
may have seemed to them. Almost like the nearby painting
of a saint praying to a statue of a saint, they face each other
in reverential silence, the material so slight between us,
a breath or the barest gesture, could disturb the air.
They seem almost stalled here, never having known death,
yet lingering too close to life, and I hear it like a music at work
in the materials, a kind of sympathetic magic, in the dead
Christ of cork & horn, in the goldleaf & velvet queen.
And it's there in the slush wax flesh of the anonymous,
Anatomical Venus, lying in repose, with her open heart,
on her pillows of silk & lace. A song as much in Salome's
demoniac eyes of shell & amber, as in the écorché of the day-
laborer's life-size red frame, made up of painted plaster
& papier-mâché. And how often through wealth & ease,
& how often through need, or whatever was ready-to-hand,
seems legible not in craft or lack thereof, but in this
more elemental grammar. I must have been looking for you
then, counting out my money, paying for the "Autobiography
of Alice B. Toklas," at the outdoor bookstore on the corner
of the park after close. I must've needed to see your face,
because there you were, two years gone this September,
standing in light filtered through the leaves, just a few tables
off, hunched over a stack of poetry, in the figure of a stranger.

COLUMBARIUM
Meghann Plunkett

When Amy held my head underwater
            I thought of the ashes—
      for generations our family urns turned
over into the pond. The dust of us
            floating and dissolving
      into brackish water. It was a game—
I pulled Amy's hair, our legs scrambling
            in a frantic treading
      of water. Small yelps bloated with laughter
and fear. Our new breasts hard against the other's back
            as we tried to sink like
      stones—afraid and alive and in love
with the idea of going too far. Thrashing
            until we couldn't breathe. It was boredom
      or something more. Our small lives blimped
with restlessness. Waves of foam gathering
            at our waistline. And the church
      down the road trotting their congregation
to the water's edge, one by one heads tilted backward.
            What more can I say
      about the doom of a body?
A lineage of women pruned into my skin.
            Pieces of them grown into the reeds.
      Stuck to a heron's foot.
A school of minnows twisting around our struggle
            and I am held under again—
      this time too long. The muffle of my own
voice. My world muted. My lungs
            open and filling.

THE RED DRESS
Meghann Plunkett

And I think of the doe. Her flank clipped, azalea-red
        against snow on the dunes of the beach.
Too many—the county set the hunters loose, extended
        the season. I think of the way her hooves staggered,
the joint of each leg trembling in snared spasm. And her breath,
        how it pillowed against the paleness. Foaming,
the ocean louder than whatever groan snarled from her throat.
        I remember the ash of that winter and how the second
shot thrummed. Brief, staccato, all the way across
        the bay we saw her knees folding in—
kicking and kicking—forgive me. It was beautiful.

Memorial Day, Monongahela Cemetery
Marty Saunders

Do we stitch shut the mouths of the dead
                    to teach them to listen—to stop their talking?

I pull out the trowel & watering can: my father & I
                    brought to our knees again, to dig & pack dirt

around petunias. Down the hill in Braddock,
                    mud-splashed t-shirts, pop bottles, & blown tires

tangle with the chest-high briars between buildings.
                    First Episcopal stripped & sold the stained glass

for rent money. The last bank closed.
                    Driving up the road, I saw sheets on a clothesline flap

with the shrieking & laughter of women who left.
                    The dead are helpless & quilted underfoot.

The moist soil swarms with nematodes & protozoa,
                    night crawlers writhing their bodies of fused rings

& little bristles. & because she must miss so many things,
                    today at her grave I leave a fallen sparrow, a little jar

containing cricket sounds, & the colored stones
                    that pressed against her throat & wrists. I leave

the lock of shock-white hair my father cut
                    from her corpse, the jewelry box filled

with her children's baby teeth. Isn't this what it is
                              to be incomplete? Think of how many years

it will be until a root's finger taps
                              through the coffin, the first thing in eternity

to touch her face.

WE ARE POETS
Kim Addonizio

We sit in a room at a desk, or maybe at an old door on sawhorses that serves as one, or maybe we have a closet or a corner to work in. We call it work: trying to think of the right adjective for a tomato, a rhinoceros, a body part. Counting syllables under our breath. Staring into the leaky void and trying to fill it faster than it empties. We need a metaphor for the moon—the bald moon that's been described so often and looks down at us amused that we are still after all these years trying to say something about it because don't we still care about the moon, and isn't it still up there, even though the scientists say it's slipping away from us, farther into space, year by year? We adore the moon. We loathe the moon, the golf ball eyeball breath mint death pill moon, the slice and fingernail and sliver on which a Hummel figurine of a boy sits fishing among the stars that we also adore and loathe while they go on twinkling and shining and blazing their dead metaphorical light into our dazed brains. For we are dazed; we are stupefied. We have heard too much and read too much and we know about the timeless subjects that are ours and the time-bound lives we have to make them new.

In cafés, we hunch over our notebooks or laptops in the classic posture of our tribe, tuning out the conversations or eavesdropping for language we can steal. For we are thieves, snapping up words and images like bats skimming over the river in the evening when the gnats are plentiful. We raid the dictionary, the thesaurus, the billboard, the scientific article. We gawk at accidents, to take away the crumped metal and shattered windshields. A gaudy piñata split open on the highway median: its treasures are ours. We hike down into the crevasses of our lives and write that our father was distant and our mother unfulfilled, that the funeral descended into drunkenness and the trip to Hawaii was the end of the marriage. We listen to the snake-kiss tape hiss of the past, to radioactive tumbleweeds being blown across the plains, to the hooves of pygmy horses that once roamed the valley after the oceans receded. We encounter creatures in the underworld and migrants crossing the river, and we follow that river into loneliness and death. There is clearly something very wrong with us.

We go to workshops, where we read our poems aloud to each other to see what is wrong with them, hoping there is nothing wrong, but like us, our poems are flawed.

Someone suggests removing a comma and then the opening three stanzas, and someone else wants more about the turtle and the roommate, and a third thinks the Bataan Death March metaphor is melodramatic, so we go home and write again about the end of the marriage and the distant father as the behemoth moon rises over the radioactive river. We try to understand the unknowable minds of editors. What made them choose from an avalanche of submissions a particularly chilly fog of words, numbing to the touch, the language baffling or insipid or patently dull? And though no one will buy us but us, we produce slim overpriced volumes and hope they will find a space in the local bookstore, where a handful of dead poets have passed into obscure immortality, twinkling and blazing on a back shelf.

We love the poets who are no longer here. We gaze at their images on book jackets and their death masks behind glass and we visit their graves and leave a stone or flower and sometimes say one of their poems back to them wondering if they can hear it under the earth because this is what poets do, wonder, and we open their books to hear what they say to us about timeless things. We long to know them, to share a glass of ale in a gone tavern or wander through the Lake District or stand beside them listening to ghosts in the rain or the wind across the steppes. We want to rescue them from the humiliating job or the forced march or the firing squad or their madness, to lull with them as the grass bows down and bring them a sunflower and recite a sutra and follow them to Siberia, Persia, Montana and Cho-fu-sa. We love their prayers and blues and jugs of intelligent wine and even their black milk. Someone has to drink it.

When we are alone, confused, aimless, desperate—which we are often—these poets comfort us. Unlike the distant father (but maybe he was in another way too close, and we write about that), unlike the unfulfilled mother (who was on second thought too selfish to notice us and here are the words to say so), unlike the terrible lovers and power-mad rulers, the spirits speak to us and wait for us to answer. For the failures of love and humanity are ongoing and legion, and require more words from us to count the ways.

To many we may seem mythical creatures, though like you we stew in traffic jams and grow bored in waiting rooms and fill with dread as the dental assistant approaches. We walk among you at the city park with our dogs and plastic bags for waste. We are there in the artichoke fields and the hospital rooms, and in the grain silo in winter, when the mice burrow in and the train takes the bend with a shrieking of brakes and the motel ice machine on the highway unloads its cold sorrow into your waiting bucket. We stand behind you in the grocery checkout line, studying your big bottle of Tito's vodka, your bag of Fritos Scoops, your frozen four-cheese pizza with the cauliflower crust. Or it could be that those are our purchases. Sometimes it is difficult to know where we end and you begin, for we are poets, everywhere and in every time. We are often invisible, often unheard, but we labor to make our melodies as sweet as we can, and we play them for love, and for you.

FOUR POEMS
Audrey Molloy

ELEGY FOR A LIMB

I'd forgotten how he takes his tea.
You'd think fourteen years with a man
would leave an imprint as detailed
as the fossil filaments of a feather;
the contours of his hands,
the half-moons of his fingernails.
Fingers are square, the jeweller said,
not round, if you look closely,
so he made him a square ring,
white gold with a dark sapphire.
The children said he lost it in the sea.

No milk, his hand blocks the cup.
Say hello to your mother from me, I want to say,
leaving your in-laws—almost as hard
as the rest of it; wounds that bleed for years,
amputations—missing fingers that still
twitch and drum, rub the edge of garments,
lost toes that tip you in their absence,
loosen your grip on things.

That Christmas after the split,
when we spent the day together
like nothing had happened;
their solemn faces on the screen after lunch,
Granny, older somehow; and the brother—
the gift of a brother in my family of sisters;
and the others, unable to smile

at the sight of the woman who left him,
even though there I was
with the children in their Kennedy clothes,
and the carcass of a bird
on the dining table I would leave
behind that evening and never see again.

Say hello to them for me.

I know he won't. In time they'll fade,
as the phantom itch fades on the sole
of a long-since severed foot.

15°

when—after the first time we made love—I could hear Puccini for days,
rising in cafés, shops, tear ducts, like the echo of dawn

30°

when you told me afterwards, propped on your elbow in half-moon light,
that your friends wouldn't believe it—you never dated tall women

45°

when—eyes glued to inflight magazines on takeoff, our forearms
just touching—I finally understood the meaning of *frisson*

60°

when your mouth arched, so proud in our wedding photo,
like the silk ballet slipper peeking from the hem of my gown

75°

when they let us take her home that newly-washed day in May,
a comma tucked in a rainbow-striped blanket

90°

when we teetered at the summit, weightless, wondering why
intimacy was forgotten long before children wore us down

105°

when I first realised that our tenth anniversary would never clear
the horizon and silently relinquished every artefact in the house

120°

when I stared at the framed maps of our home counties that spanned
an island, until a crack in my chest triggered the avalanche

135°

when the doorway framed you, the day our dog died,
my ribs decompressing from the tightness of your hug as I left

150°

when my heart slid hard against those same ribs as my key
wouldn't turn in the lead-lit door we'd painted winter white

165°

when Tosca still eddies in my tear ducts at certain times,
though now I can listen to most other things dry-eyed

180°

when the platinum light of the half-moon reminds me that we
were once the centre of a universe, if only for a while

He said he'd snuck out for the night, that he'd recently separated from the pre-frontal cortex of a doctor and what did I think of *that*? He wouldn't be drawn on the specialty but it had to be an *ologist* of sorts—there was something of the teenage boy about his forearms, pale and smooth, his hands with their close-clipped fingernails, which spoke of microsurgery. While the doctor slept, tucked up next to his trophy wife, his ego had slipped from the house and that's how I found myself next to him at 4 a.m. in the garden bar. *You like my scrubs?* he asked with a flourish—cocky bastard—and all the while I was thinking they'd look better around his knees. But I said nothing and necked my tequila, licked the salt off the back of my hand, flicked my tail at a moth. It occurs to me now that my guilt was misplaced. I was on borrowed time myself; this would be no ordinary courtship. Reader, we needed no line of coke, no champagne fountain; it was going to happen and it was simply a matter of where. A peacock screamed from the topiary. The very best thing about a pelt, I discovered, as distinct from a frock, say, or skinny jeans, is the freedom it affords to shenanigans. This was hardly making love, but a savage mating among mock orange and fig. Damn him, he was good and he knew it; Navy SEAL discipline and a few tricks up his pale blue baggy sleeve. The stars had faded from the eastern sky by the time he anointed me, wiping his bristled chin across my high breasts, taut belly, furred thighs. A trickle of blood tattooed his shoulder. His lip was swollen where I bit him to shut him up bragging. We panted, the pink dawn backlighting our garland canopy. I didn't like it (my knees would ache for days) but who says it's supposed to be fun anyway? I kicked him off with my hard hooves, and made my way back to the bar.

They say I am old,
like it disqualifies me from living.
But I know I could beat my young self in an arm wrestle,
force her satiny forearm to the boards.

They say I have lost my marbles but, by God, have I found them,
stored away for an age in the drawstring bag of duty.
Look! There's another, an alley rolled into a mind's coil
unused since pigtail days spent belly to the lino.

They say I must stay in this place—
I thought it would be worse, didn't know I'd need all this time
to sort the flipbooks of remembrance.
I cling to nothing now—not love, nor house, nor ambition.

They say I'm to keep my mind active with puzzles
or weaving willow baskets. But I am busy hiking
over memory's craggy peaks
when they think I'm napping in the dayroom.

They say I am in good company. True, I have my roommates—
pain, like a crouched wolf,
and its cure, the balm of remembered love,
a pilot light in my heart's hollow.

They don't speak of how I'll leave these at the shore.
Even the most bereft will stop, ankle-deep,
    while I push off
in the coracle I am weaving on Tuesdays, stretched with calico and tar.

And I will turn, and I will wave my paddle.

THE SOUTHWORD INTERVIEW
Yiyun Li, Fiction Writer

Photo © John Minihan (croppe

This interview was conducted by Patrick Cotter before an audience at Cork City Library on October 10th 2018 on the occasion of Yiyun Li's story collection *Gold Boy, Emerald Girl* being selected for the library's One City One Book initiative.

Yiyun Li was born in Beijing in late 1972, the year of the Rat. She was an avid reader from childhood, reading classical Chinese poetry at home and later on, novels which she was able to access while working at her school library. She was aged sixteen when the Tiananmen Square tragedy occurred. As a consequence, her generation were inducted into the army for a year's indoctrination before starting university. Whilst in the army she discovered how easily moved crowds could be by insincere rhetoric, which she was asked to compose and deliver, because she was so good at it. She emigrated to the United States at the age of twenty-three with the aim to qualify as an immunologist—to be a scientist like her father. By happy happenstance she studied immunology at the University of Iowa where one of the world's most pedigreed writing schools is situated. She began to write. She qualified with two MFAs, one in fiction and one in creative non-fiction. Soon afterwards she submitted, unsolicited, stories to *The Paris Review* where they were enthusiastically bought up by Brigid Hughes, who subsequently went on to establish the journal and literary organisation, *A Public Space*. The friendship with Hughes has developed into one of major significance for Li both professionally and personally. Li serves as an editor at *A Public Space*. Hughes is the first reader of all Li's short stories. The stories which went into her first collection, *A Thousand Years of Good Prayers*, won the Frank O'Connor International Short Story Award against competition which included William Trevor and Alice Munro. She says she learned to write from reading William Trevor. Subsequent to the win she became a correspondent and good friend of Trevor's. The book also won the Guardian First Fiction Prize. That debut was followed by the novel *The Vagrants* which spares her characters no pains whilst portraying life in a provincial city at the tail end of the Cultural Revolution. The book under discussion tonight came next. That was followed by *Kinder than Solitude*, a novel provoked into being by Li's engagement with Elizabeth Bowen's *The Death of the Heart*.

Her most recent book was her collection of autobiographical essays *Dear Friend, from My Life I Write to You in Your Life* (taking its title from Katherine Mansfield). In her essays Yiyun deals with her troubled relationship with her mother, depression, her recovery, her 'conversations' with dead writers, primarily through their letters, journals and autobiographies, John McGahern, notably, included. While she repeats the denial of being an autobiographical writer in this book, she says that writing this book led her to admit for the first time that she is, in fact, an autobiographical writer—a possibility which is easier for a reader to presume from reading the three short stories she has published most recently in *The New Yorker*.

Do you mark up all your favourite books?

I do, it's embarrassing.

You scribble all over them and you underline things and so on?

I underline, I have exclamation marks on the margins. Sometimes I yell at the author, sometimes I yell at the characters. It's embarrassing! So, I actually think I cannot have another person read through my books because so much of me is transparent. I think you can always be less transparent when you write fiction. You can hide a few things, but when I read—when I underline, when I annotate—that's probably as close to me (as a reader) as possible.

Because, some of us grew up with this belief that it's sacrilege to mark a book. I, to this day, can't turn down the corner of a page because I was so conditioned. But you know what, I'm sorry that's how I've done it, because I think Einstein said, "How do I know what I think until I write it down?" And certainly, the way you engage with books points to me to a way of being a more involved reader, a more engaged reader. Again, how do you always know how you feel about a book or its characters if you haven't made notes or made such observations?

I think a lot of people probably do have that. There's this American poet, Marianne Moore, whom I wrote about in the book, and I really love her work and her correspondence especially, so I went to see Marianne Moore's archive, and she would read a book and she would not underline. She would put the tiniest dot with a pencil next to the line. At the end of the book, she would start to copy what she wanted to underline with her very nice handwriting. I read a few books she read and I realised, that's how she read: she was dotting and then she was copying the passages.

That makes me reflect on a recent guest writer we've had in Cork, Helen Oyeyemi. One of the things which started her writing was she didn't like the ending of Little Women, *so she started crossing out various sections in the copy of the book she was reading and re-writing it as she thought it should end. Of course, in her case, it was a library book that she was writing in, and so of course she was chastised... but, she's probably made that copy of the book far more valuable with her additions.*
There's a quote hanging in my office attributed to William Trevor and the research was done by somebody before my time, so I have no idea what the source of the quote is, but I wonder, does it appear disingenuous when William Trevor is meant to have said, "Write about what you know, I'd say the opposite, in a way, you mustn't write about what you know. You must use your imagination." Is that disingenuous? Does writing about one's own life require great imagination?

Well, yes, I think there are a number of ways to answer that question. One quote I like to use with my students is from Nabokov, and he says, "Memory is a kind of imagination," and there's another from Mark Twain I also like, he says, "The older I am, the more I remember things that haven't happened to me." I think it's an experience. I also do tell my students not to write about what they know, because when you write about what you know, you take shortcuts. I think you tend to become lazy. In a way, I think also, you become less interesting. I also say write what you want to know, what you don't know. Good writing, to me, starts with questions.

Speaking of Trevor, I had this lovely lunch with him the first time we met in Boston and we were sitting there, eating, and all of a sudden there was a woman walking past us with red hair and an orange blouse. He paused, and he said, "Look at that woman, she's so interesting, isn't she? There's something about her, you just have to watch," and I thought: that's where stories come from. He looked at that woman and he thought there was a story. But, I think, if we say we know about someone's life, that we know about a character, then we are almost saying... we are arrogant enough to say we are omniscient, which is against my whole writing principal.

You quoted Nabokov earlier, but Nabokov said his characters were galley slaves, that their actions and motivations were all mapped out from the start and there was no way they were going to divert from how he thought their lives within his books should unfold. But you have a different philosophy about characters.

I do. And yes, I disagree with Nabokov, as much as I admire his work. I don't think characters are galley slaves. I have my own theory, which is that you can never know your characters well, or well enough. I think characters are like real people in the world, and when I go out in the world I talk to people, I observe people, but I think I can only know so much about someone. Also, we lie all the time. I think there was some research group in Boston that did this research and published it in America which said, as grown-ups, we lie once every ten minutes.

They're the people next to Donald Trump.

[laughs] Yes, but I think that's the thing—characters. When I work with a set of characters, when I write a story, I often feel that there is an argument going on with the characters. The characters don't want to be known. The characters push me away. And the characters often resist being known, just like real people.

Well, I think very often it's because the characters resist knowing themselves.

Yes. Sometimes, the characters know themselves, and other times they don't want to know themselves. I like that one line from Bowen's *The Death of the Heart*. I think she described a little girl as the kind of character who would be murdered. A character would never know herself to be the type of character to be murdered, and if they did know it, they wouldn't want to know it, so I think there is a kind of pushing from characters that the writers have to manage.

Talk to us a little bit about the importance of alternatives for characters in fictional worlds.

When I teach, I often use Bowen. Bowen's novel writing tips—I forget the title, but that's a beautiful essay, and in it she says that at the beginning of a novel, at the beginning of a story, characters have a lot of alternatives. By the end of the story, they run out of alternatives, and that's how you know that it's a good book. And I do believe that's how life is. At one time, when we were young, or when we were at certain stages in our lives, we thought there were a lot of alternatives, but every time we take a corner, every time we make a decision, we eliminate some alternatives, which leads us to the end of our lives, to the end of the novel... those alternatives are important in fiction. I think, as a writer, when you tell a story, you always want to remember those alternatives.

The Canadian Jesuit Philosopher Bernard Lonergan, I think one of the central ideas of his book Insight, *is that most human misery or unhappiness comes as a result of an individual trying to pursue two alternatives simultaneously.*

[laughs] Yes, I think that might be why we love fiction.

People approach books for all sorts of reasons and with all sorts of expectations. I can see how some people would approach this book with the expectation of learning what life is like in China today. Would you have anything to say to people with such expectations, or people who might have that as a primary expectation when approaching the book.

Yes, I think that happens, certainly, all the time. No American author is asked to represent America. So, I grew up in China, and I decline that responsibility to represent China, I think what I represent is my perception of the country and the country's history. It's only my point of view. I would resist that kind of reading that says that this is an encyclopaedia of contemporary China and contemporary Chinese life. The other thing is, and I know this sounds strange, but even as many of the stories are set in China... number one, the stories are written in English, and number two, the characters speak to me and to each other in English, and only afterwards I have to think about: would they speak to each other in Chinese like that? Should I switch a word to make it less fluent in English? In a way, I am making up a world, except that this world I make up is quite similar to contemporary China.

We'll talk a little later about why you write in English. So, you've denied that you're a political writer, and I know what you mean by that. Your books are written with no aim to advance or retard any particular political ideology, and yet they are highly political in that your writing acknowledges that the restraints on characters' freedom are very often political in nature. And whilst I have no doubt whatsoever that off the page, you would have no embarrassment in being described as a feminist, I feel you would balk at being described as a feminist writer. Yet, your books are replete with the examination of issues central to a feminist agenda. In the title story of this book, two tropes of yours come together in one story, one trope being that relations—particularly marriages, particularly between men and women—are best when they are devoid of passion, most especially on the man's side. Time and again, injuries are done to women throughout your oeuvre by men with strong feelings and acted-upon impulses. Another trope is the desire that a younger woman has to be close to an older, possibly mentoring woman. Do you see how those issues could be interpreted as being sympathetic to a feminist position? But, just like your politics, they probably aren't motivated by an ideology.

No, I'm not motivated by ideology, or politics or any "-ism" except... we live in this world and my characters live in this world. I think, the closest to me, to politics, is weather. I know in Ireland we talk about weather. In China, we talk about weather, too, and in America. I think politics in China is like weather in Ireland or England. You just have to live with it, you have to endure it, and you talk about it, but there's nothing you can do about politics. That's why politics is in my fiction, for the same reason that weather is in Jane Austen books. It always rains when they want to go out and ride horses. I don't have any issue or agenda. Ironically, I think people would read my work both ways. I have been approached by readers who say I'm too political, that I'm too critical of Chinese politics, and yet I have also been approached by readers who say I'm not political enough, that I'm afraid of taking a political stand. It's not my role to do that as a fiction writer. I'm not interested in that, although I am interested in their reactions. Any time you induce such a strong reaction from a reader, I think it's a great thing.

Nabokov claimed, although never completely persuasively, that he wasn't a moral author. In your various essays, you've alluded to the fact that when you read novels as a young woman you were mainly swept away by the story. You didn't take in the social context of the time. You wrote about when you had to witness and sit through public executions, in the late 70's, you found them a bore. First and foremost, it was a bore. You hadn't yet thought about the responsibilities that everyone present had, however small their participation was in the event. That's something that speaks to me of an awareness that is very political, and while I can accept that you have to make compromises as an artist on the page for the political beliefs you yourself undoubtedly have off the page, you don't quite always keep them off the page.

I agree, and I do think that there is one political statement my characters often make which is that they don't want to participate in a public life, and that is as much of a public statement as they can make. They want to live a solitary life, they want to live a lonely life because they don't want to be part of something, and that part of something is often a part of society that requires them to be patriotic, for instance, or to participate in things they don't want to.

But that particular desire of your certain characters goes further than that, doesn't it? Because not only do they not want to present a public self, but your characters also want to preserve a private, isolated self to an extreme. A short story you had last year in The New Yorker *called* On the Street Where You Live, *which is based on a song, for me the whole story turns on an extended simile. You have a woman who enters an art gallery and she suddenly—you know, some guy gets into a conversation with her and she asks him what his reaction would be if someone adjusted one of the masterpieces—*

Jackson Pollock.

That's right, and he said it would be an act of vandalism to adjust a perfect work of art, and the extended simile comes about because, later in the story, the protagonist is attending a musical performance where an autistic boy is singing a song, and the protagonist arrives at the insight that getting the boy to sing a song— getting him to sing a song in public—is an adjustment, a vandalism, of the perfect work of art that is the cocoon he has wrapped around himself to separate himself from the rest of the world.

Yeah.

I mean, in the hands of a poet, that idea alone could be a masterpiece poem, but it's very interesting how you planted it in that story and disguised it so well that when The New Yorker *interviewer interviewed you about the story, she never raised that particular element of the story. But, I mean, this idea of the perfect isolation of the individual is very central to your life as well as to your work.*

It is, and in that story, too, I think I did struggle with the same question as the character: if you own that painting and then you destroy it, is that OK? Whereas, if you destroy a painting in public, in a gallery, it's not good, but if you own the painting and destroy it, does that still count as vandalism? Also, how much can you do to another person's life? A lot of it has to do with being a parent, bringing up children.

And taking advice from experts may not always be appropriate or right.

Yes, and I have spent so much of my life in waiting rooms of this kind or that kind and I feel there are a lot of questions about how to maintain the integrity of a person, of a human being. I think, in America at least, as a parent—I don't know if it's the same here—intervention. Intervention is always important, but when does intervention become interference, and you're changing someone's life? So, I do agree, I think for me that the extreme private life is important.

And do you think the struggle to preserve that private life was central to the depressions you've written about in your essays?

Yeah, I think, you know, again, the latest book is difficult to—if I'm so private why would I publish a book about my most private pain or most private struggle? And I think, you almost have to. It's like a counter-phobia. If you have this phobia, you have to counter it by writing about it, as a way to distance yourself from that phobia. I would say yes, I am extremely private, but on the other hand, by writing about these things, I don't feel less private, I feel less struggle.

Somewhere along the various conversations you've had about this subject, you've drawn a distinction between grief and tragedy. Would you like to tell the audience your idea about that?

Yes, I think the idea of tragedy—I wrote about Stefan Zweig who committed suicide with his wife during WWII while they were in Brazil, and I feel that people would call their deaths tragedies, and I would sort of resist that. Tragedies are for the audience, only when audiences are watching something do they call things tragedy. I don't think, for themselves, or, I would prefer, that for someone who experiences these things, it's not tragedy, it's some private grief. I even hesitate to use the word grief, because grief comes from the Latin that means burden and heaviness. And I feel that, again, the grief—burden—when we lose someone, do we want to forget that kind of pain? Does that mean we don't want to remember this person anymore? So, again, I resist using grief as well in my own life because I don't want that heaviness, that burden, to tag along with my other feelings.

Your examination of the etymology of grief also points to me that as a writer in a second language, you're extremely careful with how you use words, and you're always careful to look up words which native English speakers would take for granted.

I would say that's one advantage of my being a second-language writer. Every word is a word that I have to take seriously. I use the library and the dictionary all the time, mostly just to look up etymology, to find the precise meaning of each word, so that each word means what I want it to mean.

So, the question of writing in English...

Yes, I made this sort of very, I would say, extreme or drastic statement which is, "Giving up Chinese and writing in English is a kind of suicide." It is a cutting off of the past. The taking up of another language, not to become another person—I am still myself—but I think it is an artificial beginning. You know, when we were born, we did not ask to be born, that beginning was given to us, but I think an artificial beginning is: I'm going to use this language which is not mine. I'm going to take it and use it to write.

Also, you've talked about how it frees up your thoughts.

It does free up my thoughts. I think people would say I self-censor in Chinese. I probably do self-censor in Chinese. There are certain things I don't think, and I don't use a lot of Chinese words to describe certain things, for example, feelings, a lot of things. I think English becomes this one language: I dream in English, I curse in English, I do a lot of things—the only thing I don't do in English is, I do my maths in Chinese. I think that was ingrained in me as a child, to do my maths in Chinese. So, I think English is one thing I really count as my blessing, that I got English to start writing.

So, Gold Boy, Emerald Girl, the stories are set in China. You got the ideas for many of them from your own browsing of Chinese media. Would you be able to maybe pick one of the stories and tell us: which were the parts that were from a news story and what did you have to do to turn it into an act of imagination?

Yes. OK, yes, I know. I think maybe six stories are done from media. I can talk about a couple. So, there's one story—this happened years ago—it was the beginning of the blogging era, when everyone became a blogger, and this young woman thought that her father had an affair with another woman, so she took up blogging and published her father's name, work unit, phone number, everything. She went online to have this crusade against her own father. That's the news, and I found that fascinating, to the point that I actually followed the blogs for quite a long time. I'd look at the woman's picture, I'd look at her father's picture, and I'd look at a picture of her parents when they were young. At some point I realised the story was missing a big part, was missing two big parts. One was the mother's part and one was the father's part. I wasn't quite as interested in the mother's part, but I thought that the father, who was pretty much martyred, or not martyred but, on the Internet everyone was saying he was wrong, that he was doing horrible things, and starting from there I made up a story about the father. It really wasn't about the father. I made up a story about a man who was reading the blog. Some men would get really upset with this woman, and one man got really upset because the father's information was all online. This character, the protagonist of the story, went to search for the father and they have an interaction. The whole story came from the blog, but then from there I created the story.

Then there's another story—my favourite story—and again, it was about ten years ago... China is becoming a rich country, and men are starting to have mistresses and second wives. I read in the paper that somewhere in China, six older women were so upset with men having mistresses, they came together and formed a private detective agency to help wives investigate and to find who the mistresses were. The newspaper only gave you that piece of news, saying, "Six old women become private detectives." Now I have six women—I just thought that was a great story—I want to make up these six women, all with their own motivations; so that story came from the media and in the end I took them way away from the beginning of the story.

Trevor talked about a short story being limitless. I was thinking about the story about a couple looking for a surrogate mother, and the story ends at a certain point. I think, for anybody who understands what a short story is about, it's a perfect ending for a short story. Do you ever come across frustrated readers who say, "But, what happened next? Tell me what happened next." As if you should know what happens next... do people come to you about that particular story?

Yes, and it's funny, because that particular story was published in a magazine and it ended and you turn the page and there's a new story. I was at a reading and this woman came to me and said, "I was on the subway, I was reading you story, and I turned the page and there was no more and I said, 'What? You cannot do that to me!' What happened next?" And I said, "What happened next I cannot tell you." I think you want a story to end. You know, it's interesting you mention Trevor. I have been reading Trevor for so many years, and one semester I had two students doing an independent study with me and they would read Trevor with me. One of my students made a very interesting comment, and once he pointed it out I thought he was right, he said, "Trevor always ends the story before other writers end, or he would write one more sentence and other writers wouldn't be able to write that sentence." If you go back to look at his endings, that is exactly right.

You've made a couple of references to the fact that you teach writing. Does that activity in any way interfere with your own creative process? Do you have to go to extra lengths to make space for yourself and your writing in a way that you might not have to if you weren't involved in other people's creativity?

I think writing takes a lot of energy and a lot of brain space, but on the other hand, I do strongly believe that writing cannot be taught, so I mostly teach reading in my writing classes. I believe my role is to teach them how to read, so I teach reading, and I like that part of my teaching job because I'm just teaching my favourite stories and books and sometimes a student will not get it and that's when I go in and do a close reading with them. I was talking earlier with Liam... I taught *Guests of the Nation* many times, and I can tell you... this is my thinking of American students. Earlier on I taught *Guests of the Nation* and everybody could get it. They understood everything. But my latest experience—maybe the students are younger or maybe they are a generation a little further—they say, "Oh, we don't understand. These people are speaking foreign English. What happened? What's the history here? We don't understand," and I find that so telling about the young generation, that they wouldn't go online to search, to do a very basic history search to understand the background of that story.

Yes, O'Connor uses the word "cangle" a lot—when I was a child, a lot of people still used it as a dialectical word for "candle," because again, Irish people would have learned English as a second language and earlier generations couldn't quite get their tongue around "candle" so they said "cangle"—but I had a reviewer claim that this book was full of typographical errors, "The way they spell 'candle' for instance!"
How long does it take you to write a short story? What's your usual approach for short stories, time-wise, length-wise, redrafting-wise?

I don't write stories all the time. I am always working on a novel, I can say that, but when I'm working on a novel and a story idea comes to me, I put the novel aside and I start the story. I think I start later than maybe I should, which means I actually do a lot of pre-writing in my head, so by the time I start to feel committed... I am a little impatient, if I don't get a draft done within two weeks I get really upset, because I worry that there is something about the story that can only be alive at that moment. If I take six weeks, that one thing, I cannot catch it anymore.

So, it's almost like doing watercolours, if you spend too long, you spoil it.

Yes, so with short stories, once I feel committed, I usually finish within two or three weeks.

A first draft? Or a completed story?

I think, that is the first draft, except recently I feel—I should not say this, I need to find something to knock, I'm going to jinx it—I think recently my first draft is really close to my final draft.

That's the experience of a lot of poets I know in the middle and advanced parts of their careers. There are some poets who will take weeks and weeks to tease out what they really want to say in a poem, but other poets will get it all down in one go and then it's just a matter of nit-picking and so on.
So, are there any questions from the floor?

Audience Member: *You mentioned several Irish writers, Trevor, McGahern, how did you come to meet these writers?*

Yes, serendipity plays an important part in my life. With Trevor, I encountered his work years ago. The first story I read in *The New Yorker*, one of his stories, was set in an Irish boarding school. When I read his story I was mystified. I didn't realize fiction could be written that way. At the time I had this wrong impression that fiction was for adventures, I didn't realize stories could be like that, so I checked out a book by him. Around the same time, one of my friends in grad school—her grandfather is Irish and he gave her a book of collected Trevor stories— and she said, "I think you may like his stories," so that's how I encountered his work.

McGahern is even more serendipitous. I was in London. McGahern is not as well known in America. If you walk into a book store in America, you would not see many McGahern books. I was in London and I saw all these books facing out saying John McGahern and I thought, oh, this is a writer I've never heard of in America, so I got several copies of his books from the shop there and that was when I encountered his work… And Bowen, of course, was introduced to me by Patrick Cotter and Thomas McCarthy when I first came to Cork. Both of you were quoting Bowen and I thought, oh, I don't know this writer, so then I went home and started to read her and I really loved her work. It's about chance encounters with people and chance encounters with authors, too.

Audience Member: *I'd like to ask a slightly technical question about drafts: you almost were challenged in daring to suggest that one of your short stories had been written in just one draft—*

One week—

Audience Member: *Yes, but [Patrick] said, "And then what was the next draft?" and you said, "Well, actually, that was the final draft." I was also thinking of Raymond Carver and the whole business of draft after draft and editor after editor. Now, I noticed this book was dedicated to your editor and I wonder if you could just explain a little bit about the relationship between a confident writer and a good editor?*

It's so interesting you mention Raymond Carver, because I teach one of his stories—the original draft and the Gordon Lish edits side-by-side—to my students and so much of the original story was lost in the edits to the point that I was a bit mystified at first why Carver would accept that edit. I would not have accepted that kind of edit, because in *What We Talk About When We Talk About Love*, that story ended in a question, but in the original draft, it gave an answer. So, Carver had an answer, and Gordon Lish edited the answer out of the story. I find that fascinating and unacceptable. And I'm glad you noticed that the book was dedicated to Brigid Hughes, my good friend, as Pat mentioned, and she's my first reader. Everything I write, she reads. I think the kind of trust between a writer and an editor—I can give you a couple examples. When I was working on *Kinder than Solitude*, I showed her the beginning, the opening scene, and this was at the place where they were cremating the body, and there was one sentence… there was a woman coming in and she had a chrysanthemum on her shirt, and the chrysanthemum dropped on the floor, and I wrote a very careful line describing that flower on the floor, and Bridget marked that line and said, "Why is that line there?" and I said, "I want to describe the flower." She said, "You describe the flower to make me understand that you cannot see that flower." And I said, "No, I cannot see that flower." And she said, "That's why: you are trying to hide your blind spot with that description." She made me take out that line, and I think that's the kind of edit that I want.

Another time, working on that novel, we were sitting next to each other and I noticed she scribbled something in the margin, and it was one of my favourite passages so I looked over and saw she wrote "B.S." and I said, "That's not B.S., that's a beautiful passage," and she said, "Well, the character is lying to herself so genuinely in that passage," and I noticed she was right. Later—I didn't take that passage out—but later in the novel she does come back to address the lie in that passage. So, that's the editor I look for, someone who can say, "This is such a beautiful passage, but you have to take it out because it is B.S."

You seem at a crossroads now in your writing. All of the recent stories published in The New Yorker *are set in the United States, so do you see yourself in the future writing less and less about China and more and more about America?*

Yeah, I think maybe that's the reason three or four stories are all set in America, and I'm working on a novel completely set in America. Actually, it does not have a Chinese character. I think, the longer I live in America, the more… I mean, I can still write a story and set a story in China, but I'm equally as interested in America as I am interested in China, especially in this moment in America. It's just, it's terrible. So, I think I see myself becoming more of an American writer. I don't know what that means, but my characters are more American than just Chinese-American or just Chinese.

And of course, America is a multi-ethnic or multi-racial society. There's an interesting observation in that story once again, On the Street Where You Live, *one might presume that the character is white—she has a white name but that doesn't mean the character is white—but at some stage she looks at a woman of colour and she has this internal monologue with herself. She can't decide if the woman is Chicano, or Asian, or African-American. One of the distinctions of your work is that you have no fear of jumping from point-of-view to point-of-view of different characters. It's something that people would have been told years ago in writing school never to do—they would be told to always to keep a focused point of view—and so when you come to write stories based in America, do you consider any problems writing from the perspectives of various ethnicities?*

It's so interesting... in that story, the character grew up in a small town in Iowa, a completely white town, and in the story it's so obvious she's a white character, which is interesting because when they did the illustration, the illustrator looked at my name and thought: OK, Chinese-American. So they used a Chinese boy to illustrate the story, and I thought: that is just fascinating. Because I am Chinese, there's a Chinese boy on the cover. They tried to hide a little, I think one of the editors made a protest and said the story is not about Chinese boys, so they made an edit.

One of my students just came in the other day. She's Chinese-American and she's taking this Asian-American literature class. Right off, she gave me many theories about Asian-American literature, and being Asian-American, all these theories, and I said, "Wait a minute. When you get up first thing in the morning and look in the mirror do you say, 'I am an Asian-American,' or do you say, 'I am myself, I am me?'" She says, "I am me." And I say, "Yes, that's exactly right." We write from that moment, that closeness: when you look at yourself. I don't look in a mirror and say, "I'm an immigrant" or "I'm Chinese-American." I am me, I am a mother, I am a writer, that's the thing I say... so, I think I would write about the characters from that kind of closeness. I would not want my characters to look in a mirror and say, "I am a German-American growing up in Iowa, I'm Becky, that little white girl."

Yes, after all, Trevor's characters and Bowen's characters don't say "I'm Irish." And even though they're unmistakably Irish oftentimes, they're still relatable to a young Chinese woman who's just arrived in America.

Yes, exactly.

Fool for Poetry International Chapbook Competition 2019

1st Prize: €1,000

2nd Prize: €500

Both receive chapbook publication and 25 complimentary copies

Both offered a reading and accommodation for three nights
during the Cork International Poetry Festival (March 2020)

This competition is open to new, emerging and established poets from any country. At least one of these winners will be the highest scoring manuscript entered by a debutant poet with no previously published solo collection (full-length or chapbook). Up to 25 other entrants will be publicly listed as "highly commended".

Manuscripts can be 16–24 pages in length, in the English language and the sole work of the entrant with no pastiches, translations or "versions." The poems can be in verse or prose.

There is an entrance fee of €25 for each manuscript. Entrants may enter more than one manuscript. The winners will be selected by a panel of renowned poets.

The winning chapbooks will be published by Southword Editions and launched at the Cork International Poetry Festival (March 2020). They will be for sale internationally through our own website, Amazon and selected independent booksellers.

Deadline: June 30th 2019
Guidelines: www.munsterlit.ie

THE JOHN MONTAGUE INTERNATIONAL POETRY FELLOWSHIP

The John Montague International Poetry Fellowship is an initiative of the Munster Literature Centre and is made possible through the very generous sponsorship of University College Cork. The fellowship acknowledges the special place of poetry in the cultural history and contemporary practice of Cork City.

The successful fellow will benefit from the prestige of receiving a highly competitive international literary award, which will not only allow the candidate to spend time concentrating on their own work, but also to acquire experience in literary mentoring and the teaching of writing in an academic context. The successful candidate will have the opportunity to be inspired by living in one of Europe's oldest cities, with a well-developed cultural infrastructure and a thriving literary community. The successful fellow will receive a monthly stipend of €2000 (totalling €6,000) and self-catering accommodation. The costs of travel to and from Cork will also be covered.

The fellowship requires the poet to reside in Cork for twelve weeks in 2020 and find time to work on their own writing. The poetry fellow will arrive in late January and depart in late April. The fellow will contribute a public reading and a four-morning poetry masterclass to the Cork International Poetry Festival, the largest annual poetry festival in Ireland. During their twelve-week stay they will provide a 5-credit workshop with the creative writing department of University College Cork. Their mentoring duties will consist of devoting two hours each, per week, to two Cork poets over eight weeks (32 hours total). They will be welcomed into the literary and social life of the city where they will have the opportunity to network with resident established writers. They will present a farewell public reading at the Boole Library of University College Cork. The recipient will be a poet of international standing. Fellowship applications are invited from poets working in English from outside Ireland.

The Poetry Fellow must have at least two full-length collections of poetry published. The successful candidate will be a poet respected by peers and preferably have experience in the coaching or teaching of other writers through workshops and/or mentoring, inside or outside a formal academic setting.

Deadline: July 31st 2019
Guidelines: www.southword.submittable.com

The Seán Ó'Faoláin International Short Story Competition 2019

1st Prize:

-€2000
- 1-week residency at Anam Cara Writer's & Artist's Retreat
-Offered a reading and accommodation for four nights during
the Cork International Short Story Festival (September 25 – 28, 2019)
- Publication in *Southword 38* (March 2020)

2nd Prize:

- €500 & publication in *Southword 38*

Four runners-up will be published in *Southword 38* and receive €250 (publication fee)

The competition is open to original, unpublished and unbroadcast short stories in the English language of 3,000 words or fewer. The story can be on any subject, in any style, by a writer of any nationality, living anywhere in the world. Translated work is not in the scope of this competition.

There is an entrance fee of €18 for each story. Entrants may enter more than one story. The 2019 judge is Billy O'Callaghan.

Deadline: July 31st 2019
Guidelines: www.munsterlit.ie

CONTRIBUTORS

Kim Addonizio's latest are *Bukowski in a Sundress: Confessions from a Writing Life; Mortal Trash;* and a New & Selected, *Wild Nights* (Bloodaxe).

Molly Bashaw's book of poems, *The Whole Field Still Moving Inside It,* was published in 2014.

Ron Carey's first collection, *DISTANCE,* was shortlisted for the Forward Prize Best First Collection. His latest collection is *Racing Down the Sun.*

Kevin Connelly writes poetry and fiction. His writings have been published in Ireland, the US and the UK.

Louise Crimmins Piantedosi was born in and lives near Boston. She's studied creative writing at Vermont College and GrubStreet Boston.

Elena Croitoru is studying for an MSt in Creative Writing and her work has been shortlisted for various prizes.

Alan Elyshevitz is the author of a story collection, *The Widows and Orphans Fund* (SFA Press), and three poetry chapbooks.

Timons Esaias is the author of the collection *Why Elephants No Longer Communicate in Greek.* His works have appeared in 20 languages.

Shangyang Fang grew up in Chengdu, China. He writes poems both in English and Chinese. He is currently a Poetry Fellow at Michener Center for Writers.

Natalie Ann Holborow is a Swansea-born writer of poetry and fiction. Her debut poetry collection is *And Suddenly You Find Yourself* (Parthian, 2017).

Emma Hutton is an Irish writer living in London. She is currently working on her first short story collection.

August Kleinzahler was born in New Jersey in 1949. He is the author of 14 collections of poetry and three collections of essays.

Gabe Kruis is a New Mexican poet living and writing in Brooklyn, where he helps run Wendy's Subway, a non-profit reading room and library.

Yiyun Li's latest novel is *Where Reasons End* (Random House, 2019). See page 91 for more.

Thomas Lynch is a poet, writer and undertaker. He keeps homes in West Clare and in Michigan.

Thomas McCarthy was born in Co. Waterford in 1954. His tenth collection, *Prophecy*, is published by Carcanet Press in 2019.

Audrey Molloy is a Sydney-based Irish writer working on her debut poetry collection. audreymolloy.com.

Emily O'Grady is a writer from Brisbane. Her first novel, *The Yellow House*, won the 2018 Australian/Vogel's Literary Award.

Meghann Plunkett is a poet, coder and dog enthusiast. She serves as the Poetry Reader for *The New Yorker*.

Ron Rash is a past winner of the Frank O'Connor International Short Story Award.

Marty Saunders is from Pittsburgh. His awards include an Academy of American Poets Prize and the Shipsey Poetry Prize.

Yvonne Singh is a journalist, writer and editor, based in Kent, England.

Chloe Wilson is the author of two poetry collections, *The Mermaid Problem* and *Not Fox Nor Axe*. She lives in Melbourne, Australia.

R.S. Wynn lives in Maine with her family and the perfect number of dogs (five, in case you were wondering).

How to Submit

Southword welcomes unsolicited submissions of original work in fiction and poetry during our open submission period January 1st to March 31st 2019. Work selected from this period will be published in *Southword 37* in September 2019. Submissions will be accepted through our Submittable portal online.

For unsolicited work, *Southword* will pay €40 per poem and €250 for a 3000 – 5000 word short story.

We welcome submissions of up to six poems in a single file or two short stories no longer than 5000 words each.

Visit www.southword.submittable.com for further guidelines.

37652898R00066

Printed in Poland
by Amazon Fulfillment
Poland Sp. z o.o., Wrocław